Microbiology

PreTest Self-Assessment and Review

Edited by
John Watkins Foster, Jr., M.D.
Yale-New Haven Medical Center
New Haven, Connecticut

Basic Sciences:
PreTest Self-Assessment and Review Series

John Watkins Foster, Jr., M.D., Editor
Yale-New Haven Medical Center
New Haven, Connecticut

Robert Edwards Humphreys, M.D., Ph.D., Editor
University of Massachusetts Medical School
Worcester, Massachusetts

PreTest Service, Inc.,

Distributed by Blakiston Publications
McGraw-Hill Book Company

PreTest Service, Inc., Wallingford 06492

© 1976 by PreTest Service, Inc. All rights reserved. Printed in the United States of America. No part of this publication may be reproduced, stored in a retrieval system, or transmitted, in any form or by any means, electronic, mechanical, photocopying, recording, or otherwise, without the prior written permission of the publisher.

Editor: Mary Ann C. Sheldon
Typographer: Elaine Reid
Production Staff: Donna D'Amico, Pamela G. Oliano, Judith M. Raccio
Layout: Robert Tutsky
Illustrator: Leonard Galushko
Cover Design: Silverman Design
Printer: Connecticut Printers

Library of Congress Catalog Card Number: 76-2398

ISBN: 0-07-050795-3

NOTICE

Medicine is an ever-changing science. As new research and clinical experience broaden our knowledge, changes in treatment and drug therapy are required. The editors and the publisher of this work have made every effort to ensure that the drug dosage schedules herein are accurate and in accord with the standards accepted at the time of publication. Readers are advised, however, to check the product information sheet included in the package of each drug they plan to administer to be certain that changes have not been made in the recommended dose or in the contraindications for administration. This recommendation is of particular importance in regard to new or infrequently used drugs.

Contents

List of Contributors iv

Part One: Questions

Virology 1
Bacteriology 17
Physiology 31
Rickettsiae, Chlamydiae, and Mycoplasmas 43
Mycology 47
Parasitology 54
Immunology 65

Part Two: Answers, Explanations, and References

Virology 81
Bacteriology 97
Physiology 114
Rickettsiae, Chlamydiae, and Mycoplasmas 121
Mycology 125
Parasitology 131
Immunology 141

Bibliography 155

List of Contributors

Jane Barry, M.D.
Yale-New Haven Medical Center
New Haven, Connecticut

Stewart Fox, M.D.
Yale-New Haven Medical Center
New Haven, Connecticut

Stephen Gray, M.D.
U. S. Army Hospital
Landstuhl, West Germany

Donald Francis Haggerty, Ph.D.
University of California, Los Angeles
Los Angeles, California

T. Ralph Hollands, M.D., Ph.D.
McMaster University
Hamilton, Ontario, Canada

John T. Homer, Ph.D.
University of Oklahoma
Stillwater, Oklahoma

Thomas Johnson, M.D.
Yale-New Haven Medical Center
New Haven, Connecticut

L. James Kennedy, Jr., M.D.
University of Colorado,
School of Medicine
Denver, Colorado

John Kirkwood, M.D.
Yale-New Haven Medical Center
New Haven, Connecticut

John Kozarich, Ph.D.
Harvard University
Cambridge, Massachusetts

Ian Love, M.D.
Yale-New Haven Medical Center
New Haven, Connecticut

Lore Ann McNicol, Ph.D.
University of Pennsylvania
School of Medicine
Philadelphia, Pennsylvania

Monique Minor, M.D.
Yale-New Haven Medical Center
New Haven, Connecticut

Ronald Daniel Neumann, M.D.
Yale-New Haven Medical Center
New Haven, Connecticut

David A. Pearson, Ph.D.
Yale-New Haven Medical Center
New Haven, Connecticut

Duane L. Peavy, Ph.D.
Harvard Medical School
Boston, Massachusetts

Mary Lake Polan, M.D., Ph.D.
Yale-New Haven Medical Center
New Haven, Connecticut

William Schoene, M.D.
Harvard Medical School
Boston, Massachusetts

Richard Staimen, M.D.
Fort Devens Army Hospital
Ayre, Massachusetts

Daniel Carl Sullivan, M.D.
Yale-New Haven Medical Center
New Haven, Connecticut

Gary Boyd Thurman, Ph.D.
University of Texas Medical Branch
Galveston, Texas

Prabhakar Narhari Vaidya, M.D.
Oak Forest Hospital
Oak Forest, Illinois

Richard Weiss, Ph.D.
University of California
Irvine, California

Stephen White, Ph.D.
University of Chicago
Chicago, Illinois

Virolology

DIRECTIONS: Each question below contains five suggested answers. Choose the **one best** response to each question.

1. The structures illustrated below represent

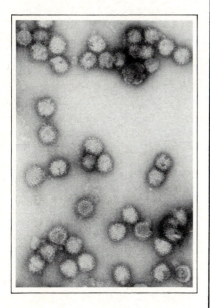

(A) bacterial endospores
(B) fungal exospores
(C) virus particles
(D) T-even bacteriophages
(E) erythrocytes

2. Which of the following phases is NOT part of the mitotic cycle of the rapidly proliferating cell?

(A) M
(B) S
(C) G_0
(D) G_1
(E) G_2

3. Which of the following agents does NOT exert its effect directly on the cytoskeleton of the cell?

(A) Concanavalin A
(B) Cytochalasin B
(C) Colcemide
(D) Colchicine
(E) Vinblastine

4. Which of the following phenomena is characteristic only of an untransformed cell arrested in the G_0 phase of the mitotic cycle?

(A) Replication of DNA before mitosis
(B) Mitosis before replication of DNA
(C) "Unbalanced" synthesis of total cellular proteins and RNA
(D) Early increase in chromatin-template activity
(E) Premature chromosome condensation

5. Which of the following cell types will replicate in azaguanine-supplemented medium?

(A) Thymidine kinase-deficient 3T3 cell
(B) Wild-type HeLa cell
(C) Lesch-Nyhan human skin fibroblast
(D) 5-Bromodeoxyuridine-resistant BRL cell
(E) Normal amniotic-fluid fibroblast

6. Which of the following procedures can NOT be used to synchronize randomly growing populations of cells?

(A) Bleomycin block
(B) Hydroxyurea block
(C) Double-thymidine block
(D) Hyperbaric N_2O treatment
(E) Selective detachment of mitotic cells

7. Which of the following conditions reversibly arrests growing cells in the G_1 phase of the mitotic cycle?

(A) Hydroxyurea supplementation
(B) Colcemide supplementation
(C) Double-thymidine block
(D) Isoleucine deprivation
(E) Hyperbaric N_2O treatment

8. All of the following properties are characteristic of an untransformed fibroblast in culture EXCEPT

(A) inability to form clones in soft agar
(B) balanced diploid karyotype
(C) reluctance to form multilayers
(D) relatively high serum requirement for growth to a given culture density
(E) contact-inhibition of movement

9. The lipid envelope of animal viruses
(A) contains proteins specified by the host cell genome
(B) contains lipids specified by the viral genome
(C) contains lipids and carbohydrates determined by the host cell
(D) is resistant to extraction by ether or detergents
(E) has a rigid structure and definite shape

10. Hemagglutination by the causative organism may be inhibited by convalescent serum in all of the following diseases EXCEPT

(A) candidiasis
(B) rubella
(C) rubeola
(D) vaccinia
(E) variola

2

11. Viral diseases can be treated or modified by all of the following drugs EXCEPT

(A) rifampin
(B) 5-fluorodeoxyuridine (FUDR)
(C) 5-iododeoxyuridine (IUDR)
(D) chloramphenicol
(E) cytosine arabinoside

12. In which of the following viral infections is the virus-induced immune response of the host an important part of the pathology of the disease?

(A) Papilloma
(B) Hepatitis B
(C) Lymphocytic choriomeningitis
(D) Polio
(E) Coxsackie

13. The simultaneous administration of two live viral vaccines may result in

(A) enhancement of the immune response to both vaccines
(B) inhibition of the immune response to one of the vaccines
(C) an increased risk of immunologic complications
(D) only an IgG antibody response
(E) mutation of one of the viruses to the virulent form

14. Interferon inhibits viral multiplication by

(A) stimulating the cell mediated immune response
(B) stimulating the humoral immune response
(C) direct antiviral action related to the suppression of mRNA formation
(D) causing uninfected cells to produce a protein which prevents the assembly of new viral particles
(E) altering the cell membrane so that viruses can not enter the cell

15. The hemagglutination-inhibition test is used to measure the presence of antibodies to

(A) cytomegalovirus
(B) herpes simplex virus
(C) respiratory syncytial (RS) virus
(D) varicella virus
(E) influenza virus

16. A medium-sized, DNA virus with a lipid-containing envelope around the viral capsid would be most likely to belong to which of the following groups?

(A) Poxvirus
(B) Herpesvirus
(C) Adenovirus
(D) Picornavirus
(E) Reovirus

17. Which of the following is NOT a picornavirus?

(A) Poliovirus
(B) Coxsackievirus A
(C) Echovirus type 8
(D) Rhinovirus
(E) Parainfluenza virus

18. Which of the following viruses does NOT belong in the same taxonomic division as the others?

(A) Coxsackie
(B) Dengue
(C) Yellow fever
(D) St. Louis encephalitis
(E) Japanese B encephalitis

19. Which of the following virus pairs are NOT related?

(A) Rabies–Marburg virus
(B) Herpes simplex–simian B virus
(C) Mumps–parainfluenza type 4
(D) Influenza–Rous sarcoma virus (RSV)
(E) Polyoma–SV40

20. Herpesviruses have been associated with all of the following EXCEPT

(A) chickenpox
(B) cytomegalic inclusion disease
(C) Kaposi's varicelliform eruption
(D) shingles
(E) verrucae

21. Mumps virus is biologically related to

(A) rabies
(B) hepatitis A
(C) measles
(D) ectromelia
(E) zoster

22. Reoviruses

(A) infect the respiratory and GI tracts
(B) contain single-stranded RNA
(C) contain single-stranded DNA
(D) are found only in man
(E) cause diarrhea

23. Echoviruses mainly infect the

(A) respiratory system
(B) central nervous system
(C) blood and lymphatic system
(D) intestinal tract
(E) bladder and urinary tract

24. All tumor (oncogenic) viruses

(A) contain double-stranded DNA
(B) produce sarcomas
(C) change the growth properties of the infected cells
(D) exist as episomes in the cytoplasm of infected cells
(E) are transmitted by insect vectors

25. Epidemic pleurodynia and myocarditis of the newborn are both caused by

(A) group B coxsackievirus
(B) polyomavirus
(C) RS virus
(D) reovirus
(E) cytomegalovirus

26. Exanthem subitum (roseola infantum) is associated with all of the following EXCEPT

(A) occasionally fatal cases
(B) an incubation period of 10 to 14 days
(C) lymphadenopathy
(D) usual occurrence in infants between 6 months and 3 years of age
(E) rubelliform rash

27. Warts are caused most frequently by which virus group?

(A) Adenovirus
(B) Picornavirus
(C) Poxvirus
(D) Papovavirus
(E) Herpesvirus

28. Echoviruses

(A) cause no human disease
(B) cause aseptic meningitis
(C) are rarely found in the gastrointestinal tract
(D) contain single-stranded DNA
(E) have a single immunologic type

29. Viral hepatitis type A is characterized by

(A) an incubation period of 48 to 180 days
(B) a solely fecal-oral infection route
(C) the presence of Australia antigen in the serum
(D) an increased IgM level
(E) generally ineffective gamma globulin prophylaxis

30. Which of the following infections is NOT associated with any diagnostic skin test antigen?

(A) Trichinosis
(B) Echinococcosis
(C) Tuberculosis
(D) Leprosy
(E) Poliomyelitis

31. Which of the following viral diseases does NOT cause localized skin or mucous membrane lesions?

(A) Herpangia
(B) Herpes progenitalis
(C) Herpes zoster
(D) Molluscum contagiosum
(E) Smallpox

32. Which of the following viruses is NOT associated with latent infections?

(A) Lymphocytic choriomeningitis virus
(B) Herpes zoster virus
(C) Smallpox virus
(D) Herpes simplex virus
(E) Adenovirus

33. Which of the following viruses causes disseminated infection?

(A) Human papillomavirus
(B) Poliovirus
(C) Rhinovirus
(D) Influenza virus
(E) Parainfluenza virus

34. Which of the following diseases is NOT spread by respiratory secretion?

(A) Histoplasmosis
(B) Influenza
(C) Poliomyelitis
(D) Smallpox
(E) Streptococcal sore throat

35. Which of the following disease organisms is NOT normally transmitted to humans from an animal reservoir?

(A) Lymphocytic choriomeningitis (LCM) virus
(B) Rabiesvirus
(C) Cytomegalovirus
(D) *Rickettsia mooseri*
(E) *Bacillus anthracis*

36. Which of the following human viral diseases is most RARELY seen in the continental United States?

(A) Rabies
(B) Chickenpox
(C) Rhinovirus upper respiratory disease
(D) Influenza
(E) Measles

37. Which of the following organisms does NOT cause solely opportunistic infections in a compromised host?

(A) *Streptococcus viridans*
(B) *Mucor oryzae*
(C) Simian B virus (*Herpesvirus simiae*)
(D) *Candida albicans*
(E) *Cryptococcus neoformans*

38. Individuals who have had varicella when young, occasionally suffer a recurrent form of the disease called shingles as adults. The agent causing this disease is a member of which family of viruses?

(A) Herpesvirus
(B) Poxvirus
(C) Adenovirus
(D) Myxovirus
(E) Paramyxovirus

39. The common cold is caused most often by

(A) adenovirus
(B) influenza virus
(C) RS virus
(D) rhinovirus
(E) parainfluenza virus

40. For which of the following viruses is there clear evidence in humans that maternal infection during the first trimester of pregnancy may result in fetal death or congenital anomalies?

(A) Measles
(B) Rubella
(C) Mumps
(D) Varicella
(E) RS

41. Which of the following diseases is NOT related to syphilis?

(A) Charcot's joint
(B) Condyloma acuminata
(C) Condyloma latum
(D) Paresis
(E) Tabes dorsalis

42. The most effective preventive measure for rubeola is

(A) antitoxin
(B) convalescent serum
(C) gamma globulin
(D) killed measles virus vaccine
(E) live attenuated measles virus vaccine

43. Australia antigen [hepatitis-associated antigen (HAA), SH, or HB antigen] is found in

(A) the blood of all Australian aborigines
(B) the blood of many patients with infectious (A) hepatitis
(C) the feces of many patients with infectious (A) hepatitis
(D) the blood of many patients with serum (B) hepatitis
(E) the blood of many patients with chemical hepatitis

44. Inflammation of which of the following organs is LEAST frequently seen in mumps infection?

(A) Kidney
(B) Ovary
(C) Pancreas
(D) Sublingual gland
(E) Testis

45. An initial smallpox vaccination normally produces maximal local reaction in

(A) 1-2 days
(B) 3-4 days
(C) 5-7 days
(D) 8-12 days
(E) three weeks

46. The congenital rubella syndrome does NOT include

(A) cataracts
(B) deafness
(C) decreased IgM levels
(D) hepatosplenomegaly
(E) patent ductus arteriosus

47. Negri bodies are characteristic of

(A) toxoplasmosis
(B) neurosyphilis
(C) congenital rubella
(D) aseptic meningitis
(E) none of the above

48. In the aseptic meningitis syndrome,

(A) the peripheral white count is elevated
(B) lymphocytes dominate in the spinal fluid during the first 24 hours
(C) the spinal fluid has an elevated glucose level
(D) WBC count of 2000 in the spinal fluid suggests lymphocytic choriomeningitis
(E) eosinophilia may indicate *Mycoplasma* infection

49. Of the following five stages of smallpox infection, which is the third or middle stage?

(A) Crusting
(B) Maculopapular
(C) Pre-eruptive
(D) Pustular
(E) Vesicular

50. Dengue fever in its early stages is characterized by

(A) pustules
(B) wheal and flare reactions
(C) edema
(D) punctiform rash
(E) severe respiratory paralysis

51. A 17-year-old female college student has splenomegaly, an elevated white cell count, heterophil antibodies, and Downey lymphocytes. She probably has

(A) gonorrhea
(B) typhus
(C) tuberculosis
(D) infectious mononucleosis
(E) syphilis

52. Influenza virus infections

(A) have a high case-fatality rate
(B) confer type-specific immunity
(C) are frequently transmitted from infected household pets
(D) commonly persist in human carriers
(E) are more severe when the organism is type B

53. Most poliovirus infections

(A) lead to residual neurologic sequellae
(B) are associated with chimpanzees
(C) disseminate through autonomic nerve ganglia
(D) are inapparent
(E) can be treated with transfer factor

54. Which of the following clinical syndromes is most commonly associated with rhinovirus infection in an adult?

(A) Bronchitis
(B) Bronchiolitis
(C) Bronchopneumonia
(D) Croup
(E) Common cold

55. Examination of a Giemsa-stained smear from scrapings at the base of a skin lesion may help to differentiate chickenpox (varicella) from smallpox (variola). Which of the following would be observed in chickenpox?

(A) Eosinophilic intranuclear inclusion bodies
(B) Eosinophilic intranuclear inclusion bodies and basophilic cytoplasmic inclusion bodies
(C) Eosinophilic cytoplasmic inclusion bodies
(D) Large syncytial masses
(E) The absence of multinuclear giant cells

SUMMARY OF DIRECTIONS

A	B	C	D	E
1, 2, 3 only	1, 3 only	2, 4 only	4 only	All are correct

88. Influenza viruses

(1) have three major serologic types, A, B, and C
(2) cause synergistic infections with *Hemophilus influenzae*
(3) have a hemagglutinin and neuraminidase subunit
(4) occur naturally only in man

89. The parainfluenza viruses

(1) both lyse and agglutinate erythrocytes
(2) all share a common antigen with mumps virus
(3) produce infections throughout the year
(4) are all cytopathic

90. Coxsackievirus is known to cause

(1) pleurodynia
(2) herpangina
(3) myocarditis in adults
(4) vomiting in infants

91. Characteristic findings with smallpox include

(1) lesions in different stages in an affected area
(2) Guarnieri bodies
(3) nuclear inclusions
(4) hyperplasia of the reticuloendothelial system

92. Measles (rubeola) virus infection

(1) may cause subacute sclerosing panencephalitis (SSPE)
(2) can be diagnosed by the presence of Koplik spots
(3) may cause giant cell pneumonia
(4) is complicated by encephalomyelitis in approximately 10 percent of cases

93. Molluscum contagiosum virus

(1) has been transmitted experimentally to man
(2) has a different appearance than other poxviruses by electron microscopy
(3) produces proliferative lesions on genital epithelium
(4) usually infects older people

94. Adenoviruses

(1) are cytopathic for human kidney cultures
(2) grow more rapidly in epithelial cells than in fibroblasts
(3) which cause disease, have shorter growth cycles than those which do not cause disease
(4) produce rounded intranuclear inclusions in HeLa cells

95. Acute herpetic gingivostomatitis (Vincent's stomatitis)

(1) has an incubation period of two weeks
(2) usually does not cause fever
(3) is most common in adolescents
(4) causes regional lymphadenitis

SUMMARY OF DIRECTIONS				
A	B	C	D	E
1, 2, 3 only	1, 3 only	2, 4 only	4 only	All are correct

96. Herpes zoster virus

(1) fails to induce disease in laboratory animals
(2) produces inclusion bodies in cultures of human embryonic tissue
(3) can be obtained from fluid from infected thyroid cells
(4) has a colchicine-like effect on human cells

97. Mumps virus infection is

(1) frequently associated with unilateral parotitis and infection on the other side can occur several years later
(2) a leading cause of male sterility due to orchitis
(3) maintained in a large canine reservoir
(4) preventable by immunization

98. Poliovirus infection

(1) only rarely is associated with paralysis
(2) is transmitted by inhalation of droplet nuclei
(3) produces type-specific immunity
(4) frequently occurs in lower animals

99. Influenza virus antigenic variation

(1) occurs by the addition of new antigenic determinants
(2) is more prominent in B strains than in A
(3) occurs in both the hemagglutinin and the neuraminidase antigens
(4) is of scientific interest but plays no role in the clinical management of the disease

100. St. Louis encephalitis

(1) causes the most marked lesions in the midbrain and brain stem
(2) has a higher incidence in children and infants than in adults
(3) has an incubation period of one to three weeks
(4) is transmitted by ticks from an avian reservoir

101. Rabiesvirus

(1) is an ether-sensitive RNA virus
(2) transmitted by bats, may cause an atypical form of the disease
(3) produces Negri bodies, cytoplasmic inclusion bodies, in nerve cells
(4) has an incubation period in humans of seven to ten days

102. Herpes simplex virus infection

(1) is acute and self-limited
(2) rarely reoccurs in a host who has a high antibody titer
(3) is reactivated by emotional disturbances, but not by sunlight or temperature alterations
(4) may involve the eye

103. Teratogenic viruses include

(1) rubella virus
(2) cytomegalovirus
(3) coxsackievirus
(4) herpes simplex virus

104. Infectious mononucleosis

(1) frequently occurs in multiple cases within a family
(2) responds to treatment with heterophil antibodies
(3) is most prevalent in the 10- to 15-year-old age group
(4) is caused by Epstein-Barr (EB) virus

105. Rubella virus is

(1) transmitted by inhalation
(2) transmitted transplacentally
(3) less contagious than measles virus
(4) often difficult to diagnose in sporadic cases

106. Measles virus infection (rubeola)

(1) occurs naturally only in man
(2) can essentially be diagnosed by its characteristic red maculo-papular rash
(3) can be prevented by a live, attenuated vaccine
(4) frequently leads to orchitis and sterility

107. Herpesviruses have been associated with

(1) infectious mononucleosis
(2) nasopharyngeal carcinoma
(3) Burkitt's lymphoma
(4) carcinoma of the cervix

DIRECTIONS: The group of questions in this section consists of five lettered headings followed by several numbered items. For each numbered item choose the **one** lettered heading with which it is **most** closely associated. Each lettered heading may be used once, more than once, or not at all.

Questions 108-112
For each disease, choose the source of its vaccine.

(A) Lymph from calf or sheep
(B) Duck embryo
(C) Cell culture from chick embryo
(D) Tissue culture from chick embryo
(E) Tissue culture from monkey kidney

108. Eastern equine encephalomyelitis (EEE)
109. Mumps
110. Measles
111. Rabies
112. Smallpox

142. Suppurative streptococcal disease

(A) includes rheumatic fever and acute glomerulonephritis
(B) may be dependent on immunologic mechanisms
(C) depends on the antiphagocytic action of the hyaluronate capsule for invasiveness
(D) is primarily caused by the production of an erythrogenic toxin
(E) is associated with osteomyelitis in sickle cell anemia

143. Babes-Ernst bodies (metachromic granules) are characteristic of
(A) neisseriae
(B) leptospirae
(C) corynebacteria
(D) macroconidia
(E) rickettsiae

144. Which of the following infections is commonly associated with dysgammaglobulinemia?

(A) Syphilis
(B) Viral hepatitis
(C) Pneumococcal pneumonia
(D) Tetanus
(E) Malaria

145. A woman develops fever, rash, and polyarthralgia during menstruation. Which of the following organisms is most likely to be responsible?

(A) *Candida albicans*
(B) *Staphylococcus aureus*
(C) *Neisseria gonorrhoeae*
(D) *Pseudomonas pyocyaneus*
(E) *Mycobacterium tuberculosis*

146. Diphtheria is caused by

(A) *Klebsiella* organisms
(B) *Listeria* organisms
(C) pneumococci
(D) corynebacteria
(E) clostridia

147. Which of the following agents is associated with granulomatosis infantiseptica?

(A) *Streptococcus pyogenes*
(B) *Streptococcus faecalis*
(C) *Staphylococcus aureus*
(D) *Listeria monocytogenes*
(E) *Erysipelothrix rhusiopathiae*

148. Staphylococci

(A) are gram-negative
(B) are almost always sensitive to penicillin
(C) do not ferment carbohydrates
(D) do not undergo transduction
(E) do not form spores

149. The most common etiologic agent of pneumonia in an adult is

(A) influenza virus
(B) *Mycoplasma pneumoniae*
(C) *Diplococcus pneumoniae*
(D) *Neisseria meningitidis*
(E) *Klebsiella pneumoniae*

150. The microorganism responsible for tularemia belongs to the genus

(A) *Vibrio*
(B) *Pasteurella*
(C) *Brucella*
(D) *Hemophilus*
(E) *Klebsiella*

151. Diplococci can be best differentiated from streptococci by

(A) gram stain
(B) acid-fast stain
(C) quellung reaction
(D) shape difference
(E) size

152. Actinomycetes are associated with all of the following EXCEPT

(A) abscesses and empyema
(B) a gram-negative staining reaction
(C) sulfur granules
(D) "lumpy jaw" in cattle
(E) culture in thioglycollate medium

153. Bacterial meningitis in children between six months and two years old is most commonly caused by

(A) *Neisseria meningitidis*
(B) *Hemophilus influenzae*
(C) *Streptococcus pyogenes*
(D) *Diplococcus pneumoniae*
(E) *Klebsiella pneumoniae*

154. The bacterium that most commonly causes puerperal sepsis is

(A) pneumococcus
(B) gonococcus
(C) *Clostridium*
(D) *Treponema*
(E) *Streptococcus*

155. The species of *Staphylococcus* commonly associated with skin infection is

(A) *S. aureus*
(B) *S. albus*
(C) *S. pyogenes*
(D) *S. salivarius*
(E) *S. epidermidis*

156. *Clostridium botulinum* food poisoning is characterized by all of the following EXCEPT

(A) diplopia
(B) dysphagia
(C) dysphasia
(D) fever
(E) respiratory paralysis

157. Pneumococci have an antigen that determines both virulence and specific type. This antigen is a

(A) thermolabile leukocidin
(B) flagellar carbohydrate
(C) nucleoprotein structure
(D) somatic carbohydrate
(E) capsular polysaccharide

158. Which of the following statements concerning rheumatic fever is NOT true?

(A) It is usually associated with elevated antistreptolysin O titers
(B) Its clinical features may include carditis, chorea, and arthritis
(C) It is a sequela to β-hemolytic streptococcal infection
(D) Its clinical features may include fever, arthralgia, and a previous history of the disease
(E) It most commonly affects two- to ten-year-old children

159. *Escherichia coli* will usually cause disease of the urinary tract when its count in the urine exceeds

(A) 1×10^2/ml
(B) 1×10^3/ml
(C) 1×10^4/ml
(D) 1×10^5/ml
(E) 1×10^6/ml

160. In patients with sickle cell anemia which of the following organisms is usually associated with osteomyelitis?

(A) Pneumococcus
(B) *Escherichia*
(C) *Pseudomonas*
(D) *Salmonella*
(E) *Staphylococcus*

161. Oroya fever is caused by

(A) *Bartonella bacilliformis*
(B) *Pseudomonas pseudomallei*
(C) bacteroides
(D) pasteurellae
(E) brucellae

162. The etiologic agent for tetanus is

(A) rust from metal
(B) certain fungi
(C) a strain of streptococci
(D) a strain of corynebacteria
(E) a strain of clostridia

163. *Corynebacterium diphtheriae* does all of the following EXCEPT

(A) produce a toxin that is absorbed in mucous membranes
(B) actively invade deep tissues
(C) form a pseudomembrane
(D) produce pharyngitis and lymphadenopathy
(E) infect the skin

164. Viridans streptococci

(A) produce β-hemolysis on blood agar
(B) are not bile soluble
(C) are not part of the normal flora of the upper respiratory tract
(D) are part of the normal flora of the urinary tract
(E) often settle on normal heart valves

165. Which of the following bacteria LEAST commonly causes meningitis?

(A) *Hemophilus influenzae*
(B) *Salmonella enteridis*
(C) *Staphylococcus aureus*
(D) *Diplococcus pneumoniae*
(E) *Neisseria meningitidis*

166. All of the following statements about yaws are true EXCEPT

(A) the primary lesion often occurs on the lower leg and foot
(B) it is a major public health problem in tropical countries
(C) it is a venereal disease
(D) it is caused by *Treponema pertenue*
(E) it is treated successfully with penicillin

167. After returning from Africa, a patient developed high fever, black vomitus, proteinuria, and jaundice. She is most likely to have

(A) dengue
(B) yellow fever
(C) kala-azar
(D) scrub typhus
(E) equine encephalitis

168. In infants, pneumothorax, pneumatoceles, and empyema are frequently complications of pneumonia caused by

(A) respiratory syncytial virus
(B) staphylococci
(C) klebsiellae
(D) mycoplasmas
(E) pneumococci

169. Primary syphilis is characterized by

(A) initial lesions appearing three months after contact
(B) a positive darkfield examination
(C) a negative VDRL test
(D) gummas
(E) tabes dorsalis

170. *Neisseria meningitidis* is most likely to be isolated from nasopharyngeal cultures when samples of secretions are obtained from the

(A) vestibules of the nose
(B) mucous membranes of the tonsils
(C) anterior nasopharynx
(D) nasopharyngeal mucosa behind the soft palate
(E) lower pharynx

171. Donovan bodies are found in

(A) mellow yellow livers
(B) chancroid
(C) lymphogranuloma venereum
(D) granuloma inguinale
(E) rabies

172. Which of the following microorganisms is NOT associated with Vincent's stomatitis?

(A) Bacilli
(B) Borreliae
(C) Cocci
(D) Fusiform bacilli
(E) Actinomycetes

173. *Bordetella pertussis* may be associated with all of the following EXCEPT

(A) encephalitis
(B) growth on Bordet-Gengou agar
(C) post-infectious immunity
(D) subculture requirement for X and V factors
(E) whooping cough

174. Acute hematogenous osteomyelitis is caused most often by

(A) *Proteus mirabilis*
(B) *Streptococcus viridans*
(C) *Staphylococcus albus*
(D) *Staphylococcus aureus*
(E) *Escherichia coli*

175. Diphtheria toxin is produced only by those strains of *Corynebacterium diphtheriae* that are

(A) glucose fermenters
(B) lysogenic for β-prophage
(C) sucrose fermenters
(D) of the mitis strain
(E) encapsulated

176. Which of the following findings in a Gram-stained throat smear from a patient with pharyngitis has the most dangerous prognosis?

(A) Gram-positive cocci in chains
(B) Gram-positive cocci in clusters
(C) Gram-positive diplococci
(D) Intracellular gram-negative diplococci
(E) Gram-positive rods with club-shaped ends

177. In cases of suspected shigellosis the best method of obtaining a specimen for culture of the causative organism is by

(A) rectal swab
(B) stool culture
(C) venipuncture
(D) urine culture
(E) spinal tap

178. The most common site of asymptomatic gonococcal infection in women is the

(A) fallopian tubes
(B) pharynx
(C) anal canal
(D) urethra
(E) endocervix

179. Food poisoning that produces almost immediate gastrointestinal symptoms is most likely to be due to

(A) salmonellae
(B) streptococci
(C) clostridia
(D) staphylococci
(E) shigellae

180. Secondary syphilis is characterized by all of the following EXCEPT

(A) Argyll Robertson pupil
(B) constitutional symptoms
(C) cutaneous lesions
(D) invasion of eyes, bones, and joints
(E) lymphadenopathy

181. A hyperemic edema of the larynx and epiglottis rapidly leading to respiratory obstruction in young children is most likely to be caused by

(A) *Klebsiella pneumoniae*
(B) *Mycoplasma pneumoniae*
(C) *Neisseria meningitidis*
(D) *Hemophilus influenzae*
(E) *Hemophilus pertussis*

DIRECTIONS: Each question below contains four suggested answers of which **one** or **more** is correct. Choose the answer

A	if	1, 2, and 3	are	correct
B	if	1 and 3	are	correct
C	if	2 and 4	are	correct
D	if	4	is	correct
E	if	1, 2, 3, and 4	are	correct

182. The principal pathogens of bacterial pneumonia include

(1) Staphylococcus aureus
(2) Aerobacter aerogenes
(3) Diplococcus pneumoniae
(4) Mycobacterium tuberculosis

183. Which diseases are considered to be venereally transmitted?

(1) Condyloma latum
(2) Granuloma inguinale
(3) Herpes progenitalis
(4) Lymphogranuloma venereum

184. *Mycobacterium leprae*

(1) is an acid-fast bacillus
(2) is easily grown on Sabouraud agar
(3) may cause a false-positive VDRL
(4) can be demonstrated by diagnostic serologic tests

185. Which of the following diseases are caused by a spirochete?

(1) Yaws
(2) Pinta
(3) Syphilis
(4) Relapsing fever

186. Streptococci may produce

(1) erythrogenic toxin
(2) hyaluronidase
(3) leukocidin
(4) streptolysin

187. In a patient with longstanding tabes dorsalis, one might expect to see

(1) absent deep tendon reflexes
(2) Argyll Robertson pupils
(3) ataxia
(4) lightning pains

188. Deoxycholate agar which is used for culturing enterobacteria

(1) contains neutral red as an indicator
(2) contains glucose as its only carbohydrate source
(3) inhibits the growth of gram-positive organisms
(4) indicates lactose fermenters as colorless colonies

189. The usual criteria for pathogenicity of *Staphylococcus aureus* include

(1) staphylokinase reaction
(2) hemolysis
(3) guinea pig inoculation
(4) coagulase reaction

135. Subacute bacterial endocarditis

A) usually occurs in an undamaged endocardial surface
B) is rapidly progressive
C) is most often caused by β-hemolytic streptococci
D) is most often caused by α-hemolytic streptococci
E) is susceptible to appropriate antibiotics because good circulation to the heart valves exists

136. Shigellae may be distinguished from salmonellae by their

A) lack of motility
B) urease production
C) positive methyl red test
D) positive mannitol fermentation test
E) negative Voges-Proskauer reaction

137. The fermentation data shown below for strains of neisseriae indicate that strain A is

	ACID FORMED FROM			GROWTH ON PLAIN NUTRIENT AGAR
	DEXTROSE	MALTOSE	SUCROSE	
STRAIN A	+	+	−	−
STRAIN B	+	−	−	−
STRAIN C	−	−	−	+

A) N. catarrhalis
B) N. flavescens
C) N. gonorrhoeae
D) N. meningitidis
E) N. sicca

138. A 68-year-old woman experiences the sudden onset of fever, shaking chills, sharp pleuritic pain, and rusty sputum. She probably has an infection caused by

(A) Hemophilus influenzae
(B) Diplococcus pneumoniae
(C) Mycoplasma pneumoniae
(D) Eikenella corrodens
(E) Neisseria gonorrhoeae

139. Burn and wound infections are often associated with

(A) Pseudomonas
(B) Salmonella
(C) Hemophilus
(D) Mycobacterium
(E) Mycoplasma

140. The most common site of *Escherichia coli* infection is the

(A) gallbladder
(B) gastrointestinal tract
(C) peritoneum
(D) respiratory tract
(E) urinary tract

141. *Staphylococcus aureus* can produce a severe food poisoning that is the result of

(A) enterotoxins
(B) hemolysins
(C) leukocidin
(D) coagulase
(E) penicillinase

127. Which of the following drugs is most effective against *Pseudomonas aeruginosa*?

(A) Penicillin
(B) Ampicillin
(C) Tetracycline
(D) Polymyxin
(E) Sulfone

128. The Schultz-Charlton reaction is

(A) specific for the presence of streptococcal infections
(B) specific for the presence of scarlet fever
(C) specific for the susceptibility to streptococcal infection
(D) specific for the susceptibility to scarlet fever
(E) none of the above

129. The sulfones are the drugs of choice for

(A) *Treponema pallidum*
(B) *Pseudomonas aeruginosa*
(C) *Mycobacterium leprae*
(D) *Actinomyces israelii*
(E) *Proteus mirabilis*

130. Immunity to group A streptococci is indicated by

(A) the Kline test
(B) the Kahn test
(C) the Dick test
(D) the Kolmer test
(E) none of the above

131. Which of the following organisms does NOT cause remittent fever?

(A) *Plasmodium vivax*
(B) *Borrelia recurrentis*
(C) *Brucella melitensis*
(D) *Mycobacterium tuberculosis*
(E) *Trichophyton rubrum*

132. Which of the following disease causes neurologic symptoms that are NOT related to the production of an exotoxin?

(A) Tetanus
(B) Botulism
(C) Rabies
(D) *Shigella* dysentery
(E) Diphtheria

133. Fever of unknown origin is rarely associated with disease produced by

(A) *Brucella melitensis*
(B) *Clostridium novyi*
(C) *Treponema pallidum*
(D) *Histoplasma capsulatum*
(E) *Mycobacterium tuberculosis*

134. Staphylococci are usually seen microscopically as

(A) short rods forming chains
(B) rods occurring singly
(C) spherical cells arranged in clusters
(D) spherical cells found singly
(E) round cells arranged in chains

118. Which of the following bacteria is the largest?

(A) *Staphylococcus aureus*
(B) *Hemophilus influenzae*
(C) *Bacillus anthracis*
(D) *Escherichia coli*
(E) *Diplococcus pneumoniae*

119. The drug of choice for treatment of *E. coli* septicemia is

(A) chloramphenicol
(B) penicillin
(C) streptomycin
(D) kanamycin
(E) sulfonamide

120. Which bacterial group exhibits butylene glycol (acetoin) fermentation?

(A) *Streptococcus*
(B) *Neisseria*
(C) *Aerobacter*
(D) *Clostridium*
(E) *Shigella*

121. Penicillin is LEAST effective in infections caused by

(A) bacilli
(B) gonococci
(C) meningococci
(D) leptospirae
(E) mycoplasmas

122. The drug of choice for treatment of *Mycobacterium leprae* is

(A) cycloserine
(B) dapsone (diaminodiphenyl sulfone)
(C) penicillin
(D) tetracycline
(E) streptomycin

123. The Wassermann test was originally a

(A) precipitin test
(B) complement-fixation test
(C) hemolysis test
(D) agglutinin test
(E) opsonin test

124. Löffler's medium is used primarily to culture

(A) *Actinomyces israelii*
(B) *Corynebacterium diphtheriae*
(C) *Neisseria meningitidis*
(D) *Neisseria gonorrhoeae*
(E) *Salmonella typhi*

125. The quellung reaction is used to identify

(A) streptococci
(B) staphylococci
(C) pneumococci
(D) all gram-positive bacteria
(E) all gram-negative bacteria

126. In the Schick test diphtheria toxin is inoculated into the right arm and toxoid into the left. If no reaction occurs in either arm, this demonstrates

(A) immunity to diphtheria and hypersensitivity to extraneous materials in the injections
(B) immunity to diphtheria and no hypersensitivity
(C) susceptibility to diphtheria and hypersensitivity
(D) susceptibility to diphtheria and no hypersensitivity
(E) nothing conclusive

Bacteriology

DIRECTIONS: Each question below contains five suggested answers. Choose the **one best** response to each question.

113. All of the following statements concerning the cell wall of gram-negative bacteria are true EXCEPT

(A) it contains layers of mucopeptide, lipopolysaccharide, and lipoprotein
(B) its antigenic specificity is determined by polysaccharide groups
(C) it acts as a barrier to the extraction of crystal violet-iodine complex by alcohol
(D) its protein contains all the common amino acids
(E) it hinders the penetration of large molecules

114. Which organisms are NOT lysed by specific antibody and complement?

(A) *Escherichia* organisms
(B) *Klebsiella* organisms
(C) Vibrios
(D) Shigellae
(E) Streptococci

115. Which of the following is NOT a gram-positive genus?

(A) *Clostridium*
(B) *Micrococcus*
(C) *Pasteurella*
(D) *Staphylococcus*
(E) *Streptococcus*

116. Which of the following is NOT a serologic test for syphilis?

(A) Frei test
(B) Fluorescent antibody test
(C) VDRL test
(D) TPI test
(E) Wassermann test

117. The Dick test is a skin test for

(A) lymphogranuloma venereum
(B) scarlet fever
(C) tuberculosis
(D) sarcoidosis
(E) none of the above

190. *Neisseria gonorrhoeae* is

(1) diplococcoid
(2) cultured on chocolate agar
(3) gram-negative
(4) sensitive to penicillin

191. *Mycobacterium leprae*

(1) stains as an acid-fast bacillus
(2) grows slowly on glucose-blood agar medium
(3) is suppressed by diaminodiphenyl-sulfone
(4) is transmitted by the murine flea

192. Organisms demonstrating gram-positive staining characteristics include

(1) *Staphylococcus aureus*
(2) *Diplococcus pneumoniae*
(3) *Micrococcus luteus*
(4) *Pseudomonas aeruginosa*

193. Granulomatous lesions are found in

(1) cat scratch fever
(2) coccidioidomycosis
(3) tuberculosis
(4) sarcoidosis

194. *Salmonella-Shigella* (SS) agar

(1) suppresses the growth of shigellae
(2) inhibits coliforms due to its high citrate content
(3) often produces salmonellae colonies which are black in color
(4) contains bile salts to inhibit gram-positive organisms

195. The growth of *Neisseria* in culture is enhanced by

(1) incubation at 50°C
(2) increased CO_2 tension
(3) the addition of fatty acids to the medium
(4) the inclusion of blood proteins in the medium

196. Streptococci can cause

(1) erysipelas
(2) impetigo
(3) glomerulonephritis
(4) puerperal fever

197. Tetanus may be treated

(1) by active immunizations with toxoids
(2) by cleansing of the wound or debridement
(3) with penicillin
(4) with tetanus antitoxin

198. What microorganisms are found on the skin of healthy people?

(1) Diphtheroid bacilli
(2) Mimeae
(3) Nonhemolytic staphylococci
(4) Yeasts

199. Leprosy is associated with

(1) acid-fast cocci
(2) amyloidosis
(3) no incidence in the continental United States
(4) a positive Wassermann test

SUMMARY OF DIRECTIONS

A	B	C	D	
1, 2, 3 only	1, 3 only	2, 4 only	4 only	All are correct

200. *Pasteurella tularensis* is characterized by

(1) a requirement for cysteine
(2) a variety of clinical states in man
(3) pleomorphism
(4) man-to-man transmission

201. True statements about diphtheria include

(1) it is caused by a corynebacteria
(2) susceptibility to it is diagnosed by the Schick test
(3) diphtheria bacilli grow well on Löffler's medium
(4) healthy individuals who harbor virulent diphtheria bacilli in their throats are considered carriers

202. *Salmonella* gastroenteritis is associated with

(1) an incubation time as short as one day
(2) acute vomiting
(3) diarrhea
(4) ingestion of contaminated food

203. *Bacillus anthracis*

(1) is a gram-negative rod
(2) causes malignant pustules
(3) has a capsule composed of a mucopolysaccharide
(4) causes woolsorter's disease

204. Exotoxin production is characteristic of

(1) *Corynebacterium diphtheriae*
(2) *Clostridium tetani*
(3) *Staphylococcus aureus*
(4) *Mycobacterium tuberculosis*

205. Bejel is characterized by

(1) a Ghon complex
(2) venereal transmission
(3) atopic dermatitis
(4) infectious skin lesions

206. Which of the following bacteria are nonmotile?

(1) Streptococci
(2) Staphylococci
(3) Neisseriae
(4) Clostridia

207. Gonococci

(1) ferment maltose
(2) easily penetrate squamous epithelium
(3) can not be distinguished biochemically from meningococci
(4) are responsible for ophthalmia neonatorum

208. Meningococci

(1) cause pharyngitis
(2) may be avirulent if unencapsulated
(3) produce endotoxin
(4) are associated with Waterhouse-Friderichsen syndrome

209. Endotoxin produced by gram-negative bacteria

(1) can elicit hemorrhagic necrosis in tissue
(2) can cause disseminated intravascular coagulation (DIC)
(3) is responsible for the Shwartzman phenomenon
(4) can cause fever

210. Gram-negative rods are the etiologic agents in which of the following diseases?

(1) Meningococcal meningitis
(2) Ludwig's angina
(3) Gonococcal arthritis
(4) Chancroid (soft chancre)

211. Relapsing fever is characterized by

(1) recurring fever
(2) altering antigenic structures
(3) chills
(4) diarrhea

212. Some of the common side effects of yaws include

(1) heart damage
(2) dermatologic scars
(3) liver damage
(4) bone destruction

213. Which of the following tests would help to distinguish *Diplococcus pneumoniae* from viridans streptococci?

(1) Bile-solubility
(2) Optochin sensitivity
(3) Mouse virulence
(4) Hemolytic reaction observed on blood agar

214. Which of the following organisms do NOT have a capsule?

(1) *Diplococcus pneumoniae*
(2) *Klebsiella pneumoniae*
(3) *Bacillus anthracis*
(4) *Corynebacterium diphtheriae*

215. Bacteroides

(1) constitute 95 percent of normal fecal flora
(2) are normal inhabitants of the respiratory and intestinal tracts
(3) can produce abscesses in lung, brain, and bowel
(4) are strictly anaerobic, gram-negative bacilli

216. Infections caused by staphylococci include

(1) impetigo contagiosa
(2) scarlet fever
(3) carbuncle
(4) pertussis

217. Vaccines against plague can be prepared from

(1) avirulent live bacteria
(2) heat-killed suspensions of virulent bacteria
(3) chemical fractions of the bacilli
(4) formalin-inactivated suspensions of virulent bacteria

DIRECTIONS: The groups of questions in this section consist of five lettered headings followed by several numbered items. For each numbered item choose the **one** lettered heading with which it is **most** closely associated. Each lettered heading may be used once, more than once, or not at all.

Questions 218-222
For each drug, choose its principal side-effect.

- (A) Gastrointestinal upset
- (B) Peripheral neuritis
- (C) Neurotoxicity
- (D) Optic neuritis
- (E) Eighth cranial nerve toxicity

218. Cycloserine

219. Ethambutol

220. Isoniazid (INH)

221. Para-Aminosalicylic acid (PAS)

222. Streptomycin

Questions 223-227
For each bacterium, choose its preferred culture medium.

- (A) Chocolate agar
- (B) Löffler's medium
- (C) Petragnani culture
- (D) Blood agar
- (E) SS agar

223. *Bacteroides fragilis*

224. *Clostridium botulinum*

225. *Corynebacterium diphtheriae*

226. *Neisseria meningitidis*

227. *Mycobacterium tuberculosis*

30

Physiology

DIRECTIONS: Each question below contains five suggested answers. Choose the **one best** response to each question.

228. Penicillinase from staphylococci inactivates 6-aminopenicillanic acid shown below, by breaking the bond numbered

[Structure of 6-aminopenicillanic acid with bonds labeled ①, ②, ③, ④, ⑤]

(A) 1
(B) 2
(C) 3
(D) 4
(E) 5

229. A positive quellung reaction is indicated by

(A) color change
(B) agglutination
(C) capsular swelling
(D) precipitation
(E) flocculation

230. Dinitrophenol kills microorganisms by

(A) protein coagulation
(B) cell wall disruption
(C) removal of free sulfhydryl groups
(D) antagonism of oxidative phosphorylation
(E) poisoning of respiratory enzymes

231. An agent that has the property of inhibiting bacterial multiplication, but that allows multiplication to resume upon its removal, is known as

(A) a disinfectant
(B) a bactericide
(C) an antiseptic
(D) a bacteriostat
(E) a sterilizer

232. The substance that is responsible for the strength of bacterial cell walls is a

(A) polysaccharide
(B) lipoprotein
(C) mucopeptide
(D) liposaccharide
(E) lipophosphate

233. The thin section of *E. coli*, pictured to the right, shows a cross section in which the cells are

(A) normal in appearance
(B) disrupted
(C) in low ionic conditions
(D) partially plasmolyzed
(E) sporulating

234. A highly potent necrotizing toxin is produced by

(A) *Streptococcus viridans*
(B) *Staphylococcus albus*
(C) *Corynebacterium diphtheriae*
(D) *Staphylococcus aureus*
(E) *Diplococcus pneumoniae*

235. The long structure shown below in the electron micrograph of a bacterium is concerned with

(A) motility
(B) cellular rigidity
(C) active transport
(D) cellular attachment
(E) conjugation

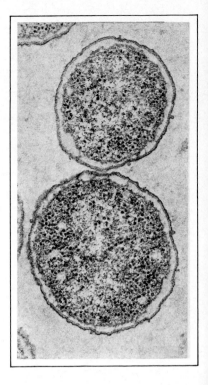

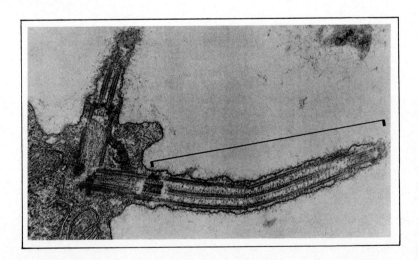

236. Swarming, as seen in *Proteus mirabilis*,

(A) requires direct sunlight
(B) is inhibited on 5% agar
(C) is facilitated by chloral hydrate
(D) is characteristic of all enteric bacteria
(E) occurs only in lactose fermenters

237. The classic taxonomy of bacteria is often based on phenotypic traits. A biochemical taxonomic approach would be based best on

(A) Gram stain characteristics
(B) guanine + cytosine (GC) base content in DNA
(C) isoenzyme homology
(D) peptidoglycan structure
(E) teichoic acid content of cell walls

238. In bacteria, penicillin

(A) has a detergent effect
(B) affects cell-wall synthesis of actively growing cells
(C) interferes with intermediary metabolism
(D) interferes with nucleic acid metabolism
(E) interferes with protein synthesis

239. The endotoxic properties of gram-negative bacteria are associated with

(A) ribonucleoprotein particles
(B) the cell membrane
(C) extracellular pili
(D) the cell wall
(E) the mesosome

240. Bacterial flagella are composed primarily of

(A) carbohydrate
(B) protein
(C) dipicolinic acid
(D) glycoprotein
(E) nucleic acid

241. The initial stain used in Gram's staining procedure is

(A) crystal violet
(B) gentian violet
(C) indigo
(D) methyl red
(E) safranin

242. The M proteins in streptococci

(A) confer protection through a polypeptide capsule
(B) function as enzymes in the transport of lactose
(C) alter the surface to inhibit phagocytosis
(D) prevent normal cells from dividing too rapidly
(E) bind chromosomes to inner membranes

243. The y gene product of the lac operon, lactose permease, is a transport protein with an apparent molecular weight of

(A) 10,000
(B) 30,000
(C) 50,000
(D) 90,000
(E) 130,000

244. Which of the following antigens of β-hemolytic streptococci is important in grouping these organisms?

(A) M protein
(B) T protein
(C) C carbohydrate
(D) R protein
(E) P protein

245. The property of both *Klebsiella pneumoniae* and *Diplococcus pneumoniae* that is responsible for their pathogenicity is the production of

(A) a necrotizing toxin
(B) a lecithinase
(C) a collagenase
(D) hyaluronidase
(E) an antiphagocyte effect by their capsules

246. Protoplasts, spheroplasts, and L forms of bacteria have morphologic and colonial similarities, but are taxonomically unrelated. Their morphologic and colonial similarities are related to the

(A) absence of a rigid cell wall
(B) absence of a polysaccharide capsule
(C) presence of a phospholipid outer membrane
(D) presence of endospores
(E) presence of peritrichous flagellation

247. In the selection of radiation-induced reversions from a methionine auxotroph, a trace of methionine is required in agar plates of "methionine-free" medium to allow growth of the prototrophic mutant. The requirement for the essential factor in producing reversion mutants reflects the phenomenon of

(A) induction
(B) mutant resistance
(C) phase variations
(D) phenotypic lag
(E) periodic selection

248. The effect of a traumatic agent (heat, low pH, or reductant) on a bacterial spore that converts it into a vegetative cell in a favorable medium is called

(A) activation
(B) emergence
(C) germination
(D) initiation
(E) outgrowth

249. Which of the following structures is NOT a plasmid?

(A) Col factors
(B) Penicillinase factors of staphylococci
(C) Resistance factors
(D) Sex factors
(E) Transfer factor

250. The surface shown below in the freeze-fractured *E. coli* is the

√(A) convex plasma membrane
(B) concave cell wall
(C) periplasm
(D) cytoplasm
(E) flagellum

DIRECTIONS: Each question below contains four suggested answers of which **one** or **more** is correct. Choose the answer

A	if	**1, 2, and 3**	are correct
B	if	**1 and 3**	are correct
C	if	**2 and 4**	are correct
D	if	**4**	is correct
E	if	**1, 2, 3, and 4**	are correct

251. Gram-positive and gram-negative bacteria differ in

(1) thickness of cell walls
(2) production of endotoxins
(3) resistance to drying
(4) the possession of capsules

252. Freeze-etch particles are located in the

(1) cell wall
(2) cytoplasm
(3) nucleus
(4) cell membrane

253. The glycocalyx

(1) is commonly found inside the cell bilayer
(2) is a component of the outer membrane surface
(3) is found in the cytoplasm
(4) determines cell surface properties

254. The periplasm contains

(1) hydrolytic enzymes
(2) phosphatases
(3) binding proteins
(4) DNA

255. Propionic acid is fermented by

(1) *Corynebacterium diphtheriae*
(2) *Corynebacterium acnes*
(3) *Actinomyces israelii*
(4) *Arachnia propionica*

256. Endospores of *Bacillus subtilis* are characterized by

(1) a lack of metabolic activity
(2) greater resistance to drying than the vegetative cell
(3) multiple covering layers, including a spore wall cortex which contains peptidoglycan
(4) a high calcium content

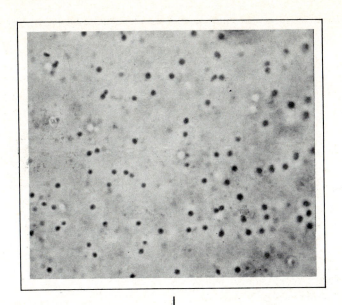

257. The *E. coli* cells illustrated in the figure shown above

(1) represent normally growing cells
(2) form after penicillin treatment
(3) result from treatment with sodium EDTA
(4) are derived from treatment with lysozyme EDTA

258. Both gram-negative and gram-positive bacterial cell walls

(1) may be hydrolyzed by lysozyme
(2) contain peptide chain cross-links between polysaccharides
(3) are constructed on a rigid polysaccharide framework
(4) contain many complex lipids

259. The number of cells in a culture at a given time is a function of

(1) time elapsed since inoculation
(2) temperature
(3) the type of culture medium
(4) the size of the inoculum

260. Acid-fast bacilli

(1) produce large amounts of lactic acid, causing acidosis
(2) are the causative agents of leprosy
(3) increase their motility at low pH
(4) are the causative agents of tuberculosis

SUMMARY OF DIRECTIONS				
A	B	C	D	E
1, 2, 3 only	1, 3 only	2, 4 only	4 only	All are correct

261. Which of the following are considered hazards of indiscriminate use of antibiotics?

(1) Development of drug resistance in microbial populations
(2) Direct drug toxicity
(3) Masking of serious infection
(4) Changes in the normal flora of the body with subsequent superinfection

262. Freeze-etch particles in *Escherichia coli*, as shown below,

(1) are exposed in the cell membrane
(2) are exposed in the cell wall
(3) appear on the face marked A
(4) appear on the face marked B

263. Acid-fast bacteria

(1) have a high lipid content
(2) can be stained by the Ziehl-Neelsen method
(3) include some actinomycetes
(4) can be decolorized with ethyl alcohol

264. Endotoxins

(1) do not produce fever
(2) are lipopolysaccharide complexes
(3) are converted into toxoids
(4) are relatively stable, and can withstand heat over 60°C

265. Which phases of bacterial culture growth have a zero growth rate?

(1) Lag phase
(2) Exponential phase
(3) Maximum stationary phase
(4) Decline phase

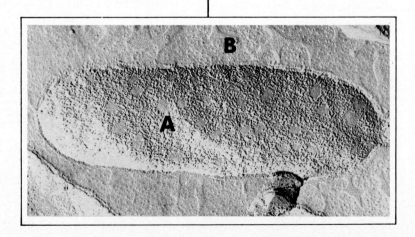

266. Ingested microorganisms have what effects on a phagocytic cell?

(1) Increased oxygen consumption
(2) Increased glycolysis
(3) Degranulation
(4) Decreased RNA turnover

267. An *E. coli* auxotroph, mutant for the biosynthesis of methionine, will

(1) be a temperature-sensitive mutant, growing at 23°C but not 40°C in an enriched medium
(2) be killed by penicillin in a methionine-free medium
(3) grow in a sulfate-containing, methionine-free medium
(4) grow in enriched medium

268. The compound shown below is characterisitic of

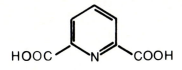

(1) bacterial flagella
(2) eukaryotic cilia
(3) mixed acid fermentation
(4) bacterial spores

269. Which of the following aqueous ethanol solutions sterilize effectively?

(1) 50%
(2) 60%
(3) 70%
(4) 100%

270. Exotoxins are

(1) excreted by living cells
(2) heat labile proteins of 10,000 to 400,000 daltons
(3) relatively unstable
(4) very potent

271. The F pilus

(1) allows cells to attach to a substrate
(2) confers sexuality
(3) functions in cell division
(4) is necessary for conjugation

272. The "backbone" of peptidoglycan contains

(1) lysine
(2) N-acetylmuramate
(3) alanine
(4) N-acetylglucosamine

273. Pasteurization

(1) can be used to control pathogens in milk
(2) was introduced to sterilize wine
(3) involves protein denaturation
(4) reduces the number of living bacteria by 98 percent

274. Sterilization by heat

(1) is more effective in the presence of water
(2) may be effected by boiling for 10-15 minutes
(3) may be effected by autoclaving for 15 minutes at 121° C
(4) does not destroy most viruses

DIRECTIONS: The groups of questions in this section consist of four or five lettered headings followed by several numbered items. For each numbered item choose the **one** lettered heading with which it is **most** closely associated. Each lettered heading may be used once, more than once, or not at all.

Questions 275-280

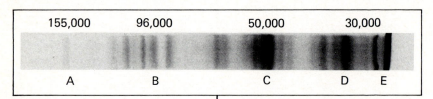

For each numbered item, choose the lettered band with which it is most likely to be associated in the 7% sodium dodecyl sulfate poly-acrylamide gel electrophoretogram of *E. coli* cell walls, shown above.

275. Lactose permease

276. Beta and beta' RNA polymerase

277. Dye front

278. Unknown polypeptide

279. Flagellin

280. Major cell wall polypeptide

Questions 281-285

For each bacterium, choose the lettered form with which it is most likely to be associated in the drawing below.

281. *Bacillus subtilis*

282. *Diplococcus pneumoniae*

283. *Staphylococcus aureus*

284. *Streptococcus viridans*

285. *Vibrio cholerae*

Questions 286-289

For each numbered item, choose the lettered growth curve (in an exponentially growing culture) with which it is most likely to be associated in the graph below. The arrow indicates the time at which drugs were added.

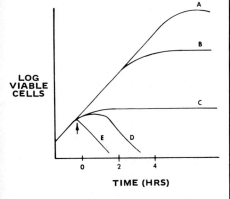

286. Chloramphenicol C

287. Penicillin D

288. Sulfonamide B

289. Control (without antibiotic) A

Questions 290-294
For each antibiotic agent, choose its site of inhibition.

(A) Cell membrane function
(B) Cell wall synthesis
(C) Protein synthesis
(D) Nucleic acid synthesis
(E) Essential metabolic pathway

290. Aminoglycoside C

291. Chloramphenicol C

292. Penicillin B

293. Polymyxin A

294. Sulfonamide E

Questions 295-298

For each cell part choose its appropriate lettered location in the freeze-fractured *E. coli* cell shown below.

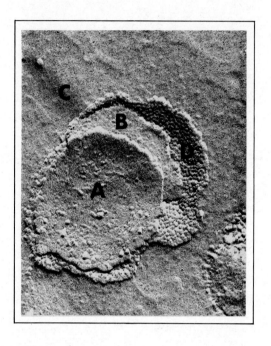

295. Plasma membrane

296. Eutectic layer

297. Cell wall (lipoid layer)

298. Peptidoglycan layer

Rickettsiae, Chlamydiae, and Mycoplasmas

DIRECTIONS: Each question below contains five suggested answers. Choose the **one best** response to each question.

299. The rickettsiae are closely related to

(A) yeast
(B) fungi
(C) viruses
(D) bacteria
(E) none of the above

300. Mosquitoes can act as vectors for all of the following infections EXCEPT

(A) yellow fever
(B) malaria
(C) tsutsugamushi fever
(D) dengue
(E) St. Louis encephalitis

301. A patient has chills, fever, headache, and atypical pneumonia. A history reveals that he raises chickens, and approximately two weeks ago lost a large number of them to an undiagnosed disease. The most likely diagnosis of this patient's condition is

(A) anthrax
(B) rabies
(C) relapsing fever
(D) leptospirosis
(E) ornithosis

302. During endemic typhus, affected patients develop antibodies to certain strains of *Proteus vulgaris*. Which of the following statements accurately explains this fact?

(A) This is an example of the Danysz phenomenon
(B) Endemic typhus is caused by a *Proteus* species
(C) Urinary tract infections occur frequently in patients with endemic typhus
√(D) There are antigenic similarities between rickettsiae and *Proteus* organisms
(E) None of the above

303. Which of the following rickettsial diseases is acquired primarily by inhalation?

(A) Scrub typhus
(B) Rickettsialpox
(C) Brill-Zinsser disease
√(D) Q fever
(E) Rocky Mountain spotted fever

304. For which of the following rickettsial diseases would the Weil-Felix agglutination reaction be negative?

(A) Spotted fever group
(B) Epidemic typhus
(C) Endemic typhus
(D) Scrub typhus
√(E) Q fever

305. What is the most common causative agent of primary atypical pneumonia

(A) *Diplococcus pneumoniae*
(B) *Streptococcus viridans*
√(C) *Mycoplasma pneumoniae*
(D) *Klebsiella pneumoniae*
(E) *Staphylococcus aureus*

306. Rickettsial growth is enhanced by

(A) chloramphenicol
(B) para-aminobenzoic acid
(C) doxycycline
√(D) sulfonamide
(E) tetracycline

307. Which of the following organisms does NOT have cell walls?

(A) Chlamydiae
(B) Rickettsiae
(C) Myxobacteria
√(D) Mycoplasmas
(E) Spirochetes

308. Rocky Mountain spotted fever is usually transmitted to man by

√(A) ticks
(B) mites
(C) lice
(D) fleas
(E) mosquitoes

309. Which of the following diseases is NOT caused by rickettsiae?

(A) Q fever
(B) Rocky Mountain spotted fever
(C) Tsutsugamushi fever
√(D) Typhoid fever
(E) Typhus

310. Chlamydial diseases, such as ornithosis, should be treated with

√(A) antibiotics
(B) gamma globulin
(C) supportive therapy
(D) arsenicals
(E) nitrogen mustard

DIRECTIONS: Each question below contains four suggested answers of which **one** or **more** is correct. Choose the answer

A	if	1, 2, and 3	are	correct
B	if	1 and 3	are	correct
C	if	2 and 4	are	correct
D	if	4	is	correct
E	if	1, 2, 3, and 4	are	correct

311. Chlamydiae can be distinguished from viruses by which of the following characteristics?

(1) Growth outside host cells
(2) Independent protein synthesis
(3) Generation of metabolic energy
(4) Antibiotic sensitivity

312. Lymphogranuloma venereum

(1) has a first stage characterized by small papules which develop approximately two weeks post-exposure
(2) has a second stage characterized by inguinal buboes
(3) has a third stage characterized by elephantiasis and fibrosis
(4) may cause severe rectal obstruction and fistula formation

313. Mycoplasmas

(1) lack a rigid cell wall
(2) stain well with Giemsa stain
(3) are resistant to penicillin
(4) reproduce on artificial media

314. The syndrome of primary atypical pneumonia (PAP) is caused by

(1) adenovirus
(2) Eaton agent
(3) mycoplasmas
(4) rickettsiae

315. Trachoma

(1) is best treated with systemic sulfonamide and ophthalmic tetracycline
(2) affects 400 million individuals
(3) is a chronic keratoconjunctivitis
(4) can occur in animals

316. Rickettsiae can be characterized as

(1) obligate intracellular parasites
(2) small rods or cocci
(3) having typical bacterial cell walls
(4) the agents of rat-bite fever

SUMMARY OF DIRECTIONS				
A	B	C	D	E
1, 2, 3 only	1, 3 only	2, 4 only	4 only	All are correct

317. The diseases which give an OX-19 Weil-Felix reaction include

(1) rickettisalpox
(2) Rocky Mountain spotted fever
(3) Q fever
(4) epidemic typhus

318. Q fever is different from all other rickettsial infections because it

(1) is not associated with a skin rash
(2) is stable outside the host cell
(3) does not give a Weil-Felix reaction
(4) is transmitted by rodents

319. Which of the following diseases are caused by a rickettsial agent?

(1) Epidemic typhus
(2) Brill's disease
(3) Trench fever
(4) Q fever

Mycology

DIRECTIONS: Each question below contains five suggested answers. Choose the **one best** response to each question.

320. While oral thrush is usually controlled by administration of nystatin, the disseminated form of candidiasis requires vigorous therapy with

(A) penicillin
(B) amphotericin B
(C) interferon
(D) chloramphenicol
(E) thiabendazole

321. If septate hyphae, 3 to 4 μ in diameter, were seen in hematoxylin-eosin-stained lung tissue, the fungus is most likely to be

(A) *Rhizopus*
(B) *Aspergillus*
(C) *Mucor*
(D) *Blastomyces dermatitidis*
(E) *Histoplasma capsulatum*

322. The actinomycetes differ from true fungi in

(A) being gram-positive
(B) causing indolent, granulomatous disease
(C) possessing branched mycelia
(D) size
(E) cell wall chemistry

323. The major cause of favus, a severe form of chronic ringworm of the scalp, is

(A) *Trichophyton schoenleinii*
(B) *Trichophyton rubrum*
(C) *Microsporum canis*
(D) *Malassezia furfur*
(E) *Epidermophyton floccosum*

324. Which of the following fungi grows primarily within cells of the reticuloendothelial system?

(A) *Sporothrix schenckii*
(B) *Histoplasma capsulatum*
(C) *Cryptococcus neoformans*
(D) *Coccidioides immitis*
(E) *Blastomyces dermatitidis*

325. The infectious particle in coccidioidomycosis is the

(A) budding yeast
(B) sporangiospore
(C) arthrospore
(D) encapsulated yeast
(E) mature sporangium

326. In the photomicrograph shown below, the object designated by the arrow is characteristic of a

(A) viral infection
(B) bacterial infection
(C) fungal infection
(D) rickettsial infection
(E) autoimmune disease

327. A diagnostic characteristic of *Candida albicans* grown on corn-meal- or rice-Tween 80 agar is

(A) production of a red pigment
(B) mucoid colony with a pigmented center
(C) lack of pigment formation
(D) production of spherical macroconidia and clusters of blastospores
(E) production of dematiacious hyphae

328. A dimorphous fungus is one that

(A) produces arthrospores and chlamydospores
(B) reproduces by both sexual and asexual reproduction
(C) can grow as a yeast or a mold
(D) will form protoplasts
(E) invades hair and skin

329. Direct microscopic examination of a sputum specimen digested with ten percent sodium hydroxide reveals an encapsulated yeast 4-20 μ in diameter. Which of the following is it most likely to be?

(A) *Candida albicans*
(B) *Cryptococcus neoformans*
(C) *Geotrichum candidum*
(D) *Aspergillus fumigatus*
(E) *Blastomyces dermatitidis*

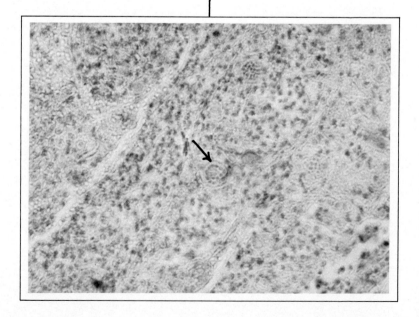

330. Finding "sulfur granules" in a wound indicates infection by

(A) *Nocardia asteroides*
(B) *Candida albicans*
(C) *Cryptococcus neoformans*
(D) *Actinomyces israelii*
(E) *Geotrichum candidum*

331. In culturing fungi which growth medium should be used?

(A) Sabouraud's agar
(B) Blood agar
(C) SS agar
(D) Chocolate agar
(E) Thioglycollate broth

332. *Geotrichum* is a fungus that very rarely infects the

(A) alimentary tract
(B) lungs
(C) bronchi
(D) brain
(E) oral cavity

333. During the third trimester of pregnancy, vaginal infection with which of the following organisms occurs more frequently than normal?

(A) *Candida*
(B) *Herellea*
(C) *Neisseria*
(D) *Pseudomonas*
(E) *Staphylococcus*

334. All of the following statements about *Histoplasma capsulatum* are true EXCEPT it

(A) assumes a yeast form when isolated on Sabouraud's glucose agar at 25° C
(B) produces three types of infection in humans: acute pulmonary; chronic progressive pulmonary; and disseminated
(C) is found in the soil from chicken coops and bat caves
(D) can be treated with amphotericin B
(E) may cause a roentgenographic picture of scattered calcifications in the spleen, liver, and lung

335. Microscopic observation of the organism shown below in a granulomatous lesion, is most compatible with a diagnosis of

(A) tuberculosis
(B) pneumococcal pneumonia
(C) kala-azar
(D) histoplasmosis
(E) borrelial infection

336. The most accurate diagnosis of fungal disease rests upon

(A) demonstration of appropriate delayed hypersensitivity
(B) the clinical appearance of lesions
(C) detection of fungi in lesions
(D) detection of spores in sputum
(E) clinical improvement following treatment with anti-fungal drugs

337. Dermatophytoses are

(A) alveolar irritations
(B) characterized by aflatoxin-induced hallucinations
(C) confined to keratinized tissues
(D) rarely associated with chronic lesions
(E) easily treated with penicillin

338. Which of the following fungi is commonly found in fresh bird droppings?

(A) *Histoplasma capsulatum*
(B) *Blastomyces dermatitidis*
(C) *Sporothrix schenckii*
(D) *Cryptococcus neoformans*
(E) None of the above

339. The most common form of sporotrichosis is

(A) cutaneous lymphatic sporotrichosis
(B) disseminated sporotrichosis
(C) visceral sporotrichosis
(D) pulmonary sporotrichosis
(E) osseous sporotrichosis

DIRECTIONS: Each question below contains four suggested answers of which **one** or **more** is correct. Choose the answer

A	if	1, 2, and 3	are correct
B	if	1 and 3	are correct
C	if	2 and 4	are correct
D	if	4	is correct
E	if	1, 2, 3, and 4	are correct

340. Mucormycosis

(1) occurs largely as a complication of a chronic debilitating disease such as diabetes
(2) may produce thrombosis and infarction of arterioles
(3) usually begins in the upper respiratory tract
(4) is usually diagnosed at autopsy

341. *Coccidioides immitis* can be associated with

(1) arthrospores
(2) granulomatous disease
(3) thin-walled cavities in lungs
(4) "valley fever" or "desert rheumatism"

342. In disseminated coccidioidomycosis, a poor prognosis is indicated by

(1) the disappearance of precipitins
(2) a decrease in intensity of the skin test response to coccidioidin
(3) the disappearance of complement-fixing antibody
(4) a high titer of complement-fixing antibodies

343. Which of the following fungal diseases can be contagious?

(1) Actinomycosis
(2) Candidiasis
(3) Cryptococcosis
(4) Dermatophytosis

344. Fungi differ from bacteria in that they

(1) contain no peptidoglycan
(2) contain sterols
(3) are sensitive to griseofulvin
(4) are prokaryotic

345. Cryptococci have a polysaccharide capsule which

(1) is an aid to diagnosis
(2) inhibits phagocytosis of the yeast
(3) cross-reacts with antisera to capsular polysaccharides of pneumococci
(4) causes a precipitin reaction with hyperimmune rabbit serum

SUMMARY OF DIRECTIONS				
A	B	C	D	E
1, 2, 3 only	1, 3 only	2, 4 only	4 only	All are correct

346. In humans, fungal disease can be produced by

(1) invasion of keratin-rich tissues
(2) contamination of wounds with spores or mycelial fragments
(3) inhalation of spores
(4) invasion of mucous membranes

347. Reproductive mechanisms in fungi include

(1) sporulation followed by spore germination
(2) hyphae fragmentation
(3) budding
(4) fusion of male and female cells with the occurrence of meiosis

DIRECTIONS: The groups of questions in this section consist of five lettered headings followed by several numbered items. For each numbered item choose the **one** lettered heading with which it is **most** closely associated. Each lettered heading may be used once, more than once, or not at all.

Questions 348-351
For each constitutional disorder, choose the supervening infection with which it is most likely to be associated.

    (A) Candidiasis
    (B) Disseminated herpes zoster
    (C) Mucormycosis
    (D) Nocardiosis
    (E) *Salmonella* osteomyelitis

348. Chronic lymphocytic leukemia

349. Hypoparathyroidism

350. Pulmonary alveolar proteinosis

351. Sickle cell trait

Questions 352-356
For each skin disease, select its causative organism.

    (A) *Epidermophyton floccosum*
    (B) *Malassezia furfur*
    (C) *Microsporum gypseum*
    (D) *Nocardia minutissima*
    (E) *Trichosporon beigelii*

352. Erythrasma

353. Piedra

354. Tinea capitis

355. Tinea pedis

356. Tinea versicolor

Parasitology

DIRECTIONS: Each question below contains five suggested answers. Choose the **one best** response to each question.

357. Malaria is not indigenous to the United States because

(A) the molluscan secondary host is not a native species
(B) the culicine mosquito is not a native species
(C) the reservoir of infected mosquitoes has been destroyed
(D) meat is carefully inspected
(E) drinking water is chlorinated

358. Which of the following statements about *Giardia lamblia* is NOT true?

(A) It is a protozoa
(B) It is usually found in the terminal ileum of the small bowel
(C) It has not been cultivated on artificial media
(D) It can cause chronic diarrhea in immunodeficient patients
(E) Quinacrine (Atabrine) is effective against it

359. An organism which is capable of living either free or as a parasite is called

(A) an obligate parasite
(B) an erratic parasite
(C) a permanent parasite
(D) a pseudoparasite
(E) a facultative parasite

360. The most pathogenic ameboid intestinal protozoa is

(A) *Entamoeba histolytica*
(B) *Dientamoeba fragilis*
(C) *Giardia lamblia*
(D) *Entamoeba coli*
(E) *Trichomonas hominis*

361. Although shown in a blood smear, the parasite below commonly remains in the lymphatic system in the early stages of infestation, and is the causative agent of elephantiasis. What is it?

(A) *Strongyloides stercoralis*
(B) *Ancylostoma duodenale*
(C) *Ascaris lumbricoides*
✓(D) *Wuchereria bancrofti*
(E) *Trichuris trichiura*

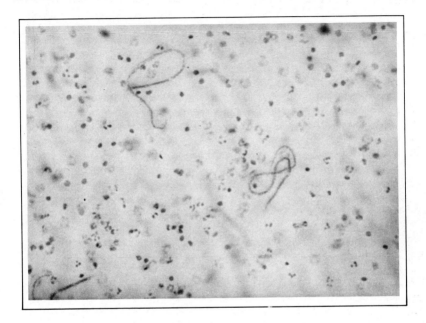

362. Hydatid disease in humans may be caused by the larval or hydatid stage of *Echinococcus granulosus*. The host for this parasite is most likely to be

(A) dogs
(B) cows
(C) moles
(D) rats
(E) pigs

363. A diagnosis of trichinosis is established most definitively by

✓(A) demonstration of encysted larvae in skeletal muscle
(B) eosinophilia
(C) presence of eggs in the feces
(D) edema of the face
(E) muscular pains

Photographs accompany Questions 364-365

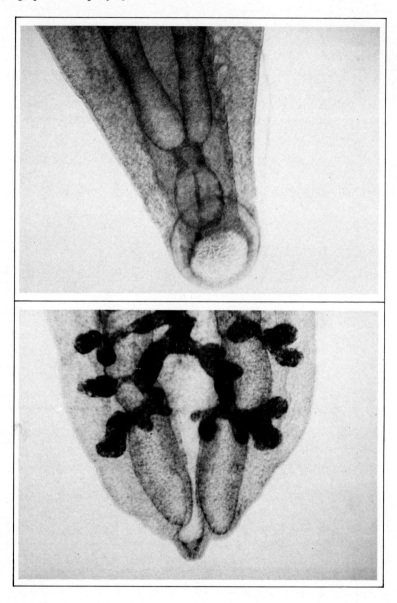

364. A young man, recently returned from Vietnam, has severe liver involvement and thickening of the walls of the biliary duct. The etiologic agent of his disease, shown in the photomicrographs on the facing page, is

(A) *Plasmodium falciparum*
(B) *Clonorchis sinensis*
(C) *Diphyllobothrium latum*
(D) *Taenia solium*
(E) *Taenia saginata*

365. An intermediate form of the organism shown on the facing page lives in the

(A) mosquito
(B) pig
(C) snail
(D) cow
(E) tick

366. Which of the following techniques is most successful for recovering pinworm eggs?

(A) Sugar fecal flotation
(B) Zinc sulfate fecal flotation
(C) Tap water fecal sedimentation
(D) Direct fecal centrifugal-flotation
(E) Cellophane tape anal swab

367. Recommendations for the control of human hookworm in an endemic area include the construction of sanitary facilities and the

(A) thorough washing of fresh fruit and vegetables
(B) thorough cooking of all meat
(C) reduction of the feral dog population
(D) use of insecticides to control flies
(E) use of footwear

368. Autoinfection may be responsible for long-standing infections with

(A) *Paragonimus westermani*
(B) *Necator americanus*
(C) *Strongyloides stercoralis*
(D) *Schistosoma haematobium*
(E) *Diphyllobothrium latum*

369. The insect vector of *Trypanosoma cruzi*, the cause of Chagas' disease, is the

(A) rat mite
(B) anopheline mosquito
(C) Lone Star tick
(D) reduviid bug
(E) head louse

370. Visceral larva migrans is usually produced by

(A) *Enterobius vermicularis*
(B) *Ascaris lumbricoides*
(C) *Toxocara canis*
(D) *Ancylostoma braziliense*
(E) *Ancylostoma caninum*

371. Human infection with the beef tapeworm *Taenia saginata* is usually less serious than with the pork tapeworm (*T. solium*) because

(A) the adult worms are smaller and acute intestinal stoppage is less common
(B) cysticercosis does not occur
(C) toxic by-products are not given off by the adult worm
(D) no more than a single adult is present in an infection
(E) the eggs cause less irritation of the mucosa of the digestive tract

372. Spiders, order Araneida,

(A) cause burrowing skin infestations
(B) transmit protozoan blood infections
(C) can be the vector for viral infection
(D) can cause systemic disease by their toxin
(E) do none of the above

373. Which of the following developmental forms is NOT associated with trematodes?

(A) Cercaria
(B) Miracidium
(C) Schizont
(D) Redia
(E) Metacercaria

374. Which of the following parasites is NOT a protozoan?

(A) *Entamoeba coli*
(B) *Echinococcus granulosus*
(C) *Pneumocystis carinii*
(D) *Plasmodium vivax*
(E) *Giardia lamblia*

375. Which of the following parasites is NOT a flatworm, or platyhelminth?

(A) *Taenia saginata*
(B) *Diphyllobothrium latum*
(C) *Schistosoma mansoni*
(D) *Fasciola hepatica*
(E) *Ascaris lumbricoides*

376. Adult hookworms, *Ancylostoma duodenale* and *Necator americanus*,

(A) anchor in the intestinal mucosa and suck blood from the host
(B) anchor in the intestinal mucosa and absorb nutrients from the host's intestinal contents
(C) enter the host through the skin of bare feet
(D) can persist in warm, moist soil for several weeks
(E) pass through the alveolar wall to reach the digestive tract

377. Which of the following parasitic infections is most common in the continental United States?

(A) Malaria, *Plasmodium*
(B) Pinworm, *Enterobius*
(C) Trichinosis, *Trichinella*
(D) Schistosomiasis, *Schistosoma*
(E) Trypanosomiasis, *Trypanosoma*

378. Observation of the organism shown below in diarrheic feces is compatible with a diagnosis of

(A) bilharziasis
(B) ascariasis
(C) brucellosis
(D) giardiasis
(E) shigellosis

379. Which of the following is the drug of choice for treatment of ascariasis?

(A) Niridazole (Ambilhar)
(B) Piperazine citrate (Antepar)
(C) Pyrvinium pamoate (Povan)
(D) Quinacrine hydrochloride (Atabrine)
(E) Thiabendazole (Mintezol)

380. What is the drug of choice for treatment of *Taenia saginata* (beef tapeworm)?

(A) Emetine hydrochloride
(B) Niclosamide (Yomesan)
(C) Piperazine citrate (Antepar)
(D) Quinacrine hydrochloride (Atabrine)
(E) Thiabendazole (Mintezol)

381. Which of the following worms is NOT a nematode?

(A) *Enterobius vermicularis*
(B) *Ascaris lumbricoides*
(C) *Necator americanus*
(D) *Taenia saginata*
(E) *Trichuris trichiura*

382. In diagnosing kala-azar, which of the following tests has the highest percentage of positive findings?

(A) Liver biopsy
(B) Blood culture
(C) Splenic aspiration
(D) Stool examination
(E) Sputum examination

383. Which of the following diseases is NOT caused by helminths?

(A) Clonorchiasis
(B) Enterobiasis
(C) Filariasis
(D) Larva migrans
(E) Toxoplasmosis

384. Which of the following organisms is NOT a microfilariae?

(A) *Brugia malayi*
(B) *Loa loa*
(C) *Onchocerca volvulus*
(D) *Schistosoma haematobium*
(E) *Wuchereria bancrofti*

385. A woman who has recently returned from Africa, has been having paroxysms of chills, fever, and sweating which last for one to two days and recur at 36 to 48 hour intervals. Examination of a stained blood film reveals ring and crescent forms within the red blood cells. The infecting organism is

(A) *Plasmodium falciparum*
(B) *Trypanosoma gambiense*
(C) *Wuchereria bancrofti*
(D) *Plasmodium vivax*
(E) *Schistosoma mansoni*

386. Which of the following parasites may be ingested in uncooked fish?

(A) *Hymenolepis diminuta*
(B) *Taenia saginata*
(C) *Diphyllobothrium latum*
(D) *Strongyloides stercoralis*
(E) *Schistosoma japonicum*

387. A recent traveler to Rhodesia complains of severe chills and fever, abdominal tenderness, and darkening urine. The febrile periods last for 28 hours and recur regularly. Which of the schematic blood films shown below is characteristic of this symptomatology?

(A) A
✓ (B) B
(C) C
(D) D
(E) E

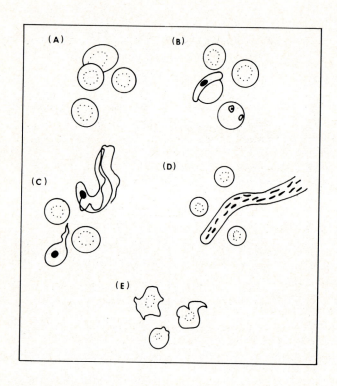

DIRECTIONS: Each question below contains four suggested answers of which **one** or **more** is correct. Choose the answer

A	if	**1, 2, and 3**	are correct
B	if	**1 and 3**	are correct
C	if	**2 and 4**	are correct
D	if	**4**	is correct
E	if	**1, 2, 3, and 4**	are correct

388. The clinical symptoms of trichinosis include

(1) eosinophilia
(2) periorbital edema
(3) muscle pain
(4) diarrhea

389. Eosinophilia is

(1) associated with parasitic infection
(2) associated with carcinoma of the rectum
(3) more marked in recent than in chronic parasitic infection
(4) associated with periarteritis nodosa

390. Forms of schistosomiasis that commonly occur in the continental United States include

(1) schistosomal hematuria
(2) schistosomal dysentery
(3) oriental schistosomiasis
(4) schistosomal dermatitis

391. The bed bugs *Cimex lectularius* and *C. hemipterus*

(1) are bloodsucking parasites of humans
(2) can be a vector for Chagas' disease
(3) can be controlled with DDT
(4) are important disease vectors

392. Human lice

(1) are maintained only on humans
(2) cause itching skin lesions
(3) include the species *Pediculus humanus* and *Phthirus pubis*
(4) transmit epidemic typhus, relapsing fever, and trench fever

393. Toxoplasmosis is

(1) a cause of serious fetal infection
(2) diagnosed using the Sabin-Feldman dye test
(3) a cause of mild, self-limiting disease in adults
(4) a rare infection in the continental United States

394. Scabies is

(1) caused by *Sarcoptes scabiei*
(2) often complicated by secondary bacterial infection
(3) best diagnosed by morphologic identification of the mite
(4) effectively treated with gamma benzene hexachloride

395. The fine fibrils (F) shown below in an ameba are

(1) termed microtubules
(2) similar to muscle actin
(3) similar to glycoprotein strands in bacterial cell walls
(4) involved in cellular motility

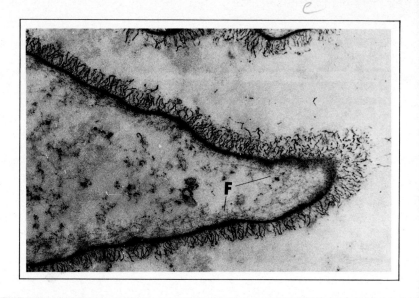

396. Hydatid disease

(1) frequently affects the liver
(2) can be caused by invasion of an intestinal protozoan that is part of the normal flora
(3) commonly involves the dog as an intermediate
(4) is common in the continental United States

397. The parasitic trematode infections

(1) are effectively treated with the broad-spectrum anthelmintic thiabendazole
(2) may involve one or two intermediate hosts
(3) are typically transmitted to humans via rare beef
(4) are rarely seen in the continental United States

SUMMARY OF DIRECTIONS

A	B	C	D	E
1, 2, 3 only	1, 3 only	2, 4 only	4 only	All are correct

398. Which of the following organisms can be transmitted to humans through improperly prepared meat?

(1) *Taenia solium*
(2) *Clostridium perfringens*
(3) *Trichinella spiralis*
(4) *Taenia saginata*

399. Helminths which localize principally in the liver include

(1) *Echinococcus*
(2) *Ascaris*
(3) *Clonorchis*
(4) *Paragonimus*

400. Malaria

(1) causes a normocytic anemia
(2) is best treated with primaquine phosphate during severe acute attacks
(3) may cause nephrosis in children infected with *Plasmodium malariae*
(4) involves parasites that have a sexual cycle in human hosts, and an asexual cycle in mosquitoes

401. A patient with sandfly fever may

(1) be cured with sulfur-containing drugs
(2) suffer damage to the pyramidal tract
(3) develop a chronic granulomatous reaction to *Bartonella bacilliformis*
(4) have pruritic papules on the skin for five days

402. Adult tapeworms are injurious to their human host because they

(1) may deprive the host of vitamins
(2) obtain protein from the host's intestinal mucosa
(3) can predispose to bacterial invasion at the site of scolex attachment
(4) produce an enterotoxin

403. *Giardia lamblia*

(1) is a flagellated protozoan
(2) is usually nonpathogenic for humans
(3) may invade the gallbladder
(4) is refractory to chemotherapy

404. Trichomonads are protozoans, of which three species infect humans. Of these

(1) *Trichomonas hominis* is the most pathogenic for humans
(2) *T. vaginalis* grows best at pH 3.8-4.4
(3) *T. vaginalis* usually causes mucosal erosion in the uterus
(4) all species possess an undulating membrane

SUMMARY OF DIRECTIONS				
A	B	C	D	E
1, 2, 3 only	1, 3 only	2, 4 only	4 only	All are correct

405. The length of the cycle from merozoite to merozoite is 50 hours or less for

(1) *Plasmodium vivax*
(2) *Plasmodium falciparum*
(3) *Plasmodium ovale*
(4) *Plasmodium malariae*

406. Pinworm infections are

(1) maintained exclusively in human hosts
(2) widely distributed throughout the world
(3) common in the continental United States
(4) most frequent in young children

407. In schistosomiasis,

(1) calcification may be seen radiographically in the wall of the bladder
(2) control of the disease depends upon destruction of the intermediate host, the snail
(3) laboratory diagnosis is based on the appearance of the eggs found in feces or urine, or on rectal or liver biopsy
(4) pulmonary arterial hypertension may occur

408. *Entamoeba histolytica* is a human intestinal parasite characterized by

(1) granular cytoplasm
(2) a size of 15-30 μ
(3) red cells in the cytoplasm
(4) trophozoites in the stools of asymptomatic carriers

409. Which of the following statements about plasmodia are true?

(1) The schizogonic cycle occurs in the *Anopheles* mosquito
(2) Coarse stippling of erythrocytes is characteristic of *Plasmodium vivax*
(3) *P. vivax* invades red cells of all ages
(4) *P. falciparum* multiplication often terminates in 6 to 8 months without treatment

410. *Trypanosoma cruzi* is associated with

(1) interstitial myocarditis
(2) Romaña's sign—unilateral swelling of the eyelids
(3) less parasitemia than *T. gambiense*
(4) the tsetse fly

411. Amebas in the human intestine are

(1) often nonpathogenic
(2) pathogenic when cysts become toxigenic
(3) a cause of appendicitis
(4) transmitted usually as trophozoites

Immunology

DIRECTIONS: Each question below contains five suggested answers. Choose the **one best** response to each question.

412. Which of the following soluble products are NOT generated chiefly by thymus-derived lymphocytes (T cells)?

(A) Antibody
(B) Lymphotoxin
(C) Blastogenic factor
(D) Migration-inhibition factor
(E) Transfer factor

413. The class-specific antigenic determinance of immunoglobulins is associated with the

(A) J chain
(B) T chain
(C) light chain
(D) heavy chain
(E) secretory component

414. A young child has had repeated infections with *Candida albicans* and respiratory viruses since she was three months old. As part of the clinical evaluation of her immune status, her responses to routine immunization procedures will be tested. The use of which of the following vaccines is contraindicated?

(A) Diphtheria toxoid
(B) *B. pertussis*
(C) Tetanus toxoid
(D) BCG
(E) Inactivated polio

415. Bence Jones proteins, which are often found in the urine of patients with multiple myeloma, are

(A) mu chains
(B) gamma chains
(C) kappa and lambda chains
(D) albumin
(E) fibrinogen split products

416. Giant cell pneumonia, a disease of debilitated children, is caused by measles virus. Measles virus also has been implicated in

(A) infectious mononucleosis
(B) Creutzfeldt-Jakob disease
(C) kuru
(D) subacute sclerosing panencephalitis
(E) Burkitt's lymphoma

417. Antibodies which neutralize infectivity are formed against which of the following influenza virus antigens?

(A) Nucleocapsid
(B) Nucleoprotein
(C) Neuraminidase
(D) Protein of the viral envelope (M protein)
(E) Hemagglutinin on the virion's surface

418. Which of the following tests is the most sensitive for measuring antiviral antibody?

(A) Virus neutralization
(B) Double diffusion in agar gel
(C) Complement fixation
(D) Radioimmunoassay
(E) Immunoelectrophoresis

419. The class of immunoglobulin important in protecting the mucosal surfaces of the respiratory, intestinal, and genitourinary tracts from pathogenic organisms is

(A) IgA
(B) IgD
(C) IgE
(D) IgG
(E) IgM

420. Children who have received inactivated measles vaccine may have swelling, tenderness, and erythema at the site of a subsequent live measles vaccination. If this reaction occurs approximately six to eight hours after the live measles immunization, it is most likely to be

(A) a Prausnitz-Küstner reaction
(B) an Arthus reaction
(C) a Shwartzman reaction
(D) a Schick reaction
(E) a Coombs reaction

421. Complement is a complex series of interacting proteins that serve to amplify the actions of certain classes of antibodies. How many of the nine functional units of complement must interact to cause swift lysis of antibody-coated cells?

(A) The first three
(B) The first five
(C) The first six
(D) The first eight
(E) All nine

422. Which of the following terms could be used to describe the transplantation of a kidney from one identical twin to the other twin?

(A) Autograft
(B) Isograft
(C) Homograft
(D) Heterograft
(E) Xenograft

423. The Arthus reaction requires

(A) more time than serum sickness
(B) more time than cutaneous anaphylaxis
(C) only IgM antibody
(D) a low level of antibody
(E) rapid liberation of pharmacologic agents

424. The immune deficiency in chronic granulomatous disease is related to the

(A) absence of the third component of complement
(B) reduced levels of the fifth component of complement
(C) inability of polymorphonuclear leukocytes to ingest bacteria
(D) inability of polymorphonuclear leukocytes to kill ingested bacteria
(E) dysgammaglobulinemia

425. Which of the following serum globulin classes would be elevated in a newborn infant suffering from an in utero infection?

(A) IgA
(B) IgD
(C) IgE
(D) IgG
(E) IgM

426. The light and heavy chains of immunoglobulins M and G are joined by

(A) carbon-to-carbon links
(B) peptide bonds
(C) disulfide bonds
(D) side chain ester links
(E) glycosidic linkages

427. The Wassermann and Kolmer tests involve

(A) flocculation
(B) complement fixation
(C) agglutination
(D) fluorescent antibody
(E) immunodiffusion

428. Anaphylaxis can be mediated by

(A) lymphocytes
(B) histamine
(C) phagocytes
(D) delayed hypersensitivity
(E) endotoxin

429. The Prausnitz-Küstner reaction requires

(A) time for the antigen to be altered by macrophages
(B) time for the antigen to be deposited
(C) time for the antigen to fix to skin receptors
(D) no latent period
(E) none of the above

430. Initially following transfusion of platelets radiolabeled with chromium, one-third will be rapidly trapped in the

(A) thymus
(B) kidneys
(C) spleen
(D) bone marrow
(E) brain

431. Intravenous infusion of which of the following hormones would cause a rapid, 30 to 50 percent elevation of the platelet count of the blood?

(A) Estrogen
(B) Prostaglandin E
(C) Aldosterone
(D) Epinephrine
(E) Progesterone

432. Peyer's patches are aggregated lymphatic follicles which are present in largest number in the

(A) duodenum
(B) jejunum
(C) ileum
(D) cecum
(E) colon

433. Which immunoglobulin passes freely across the placenta to the fetus?

(A) IgA
(B) IgD
(C) IgE
(D) IgG
(E) IgM

434. Which of the following substances is NOT liberated during anaphylaxis?

(A) Histamine
(B) Kinin
(C) Pyrogen
(D) Serotonin
(E) Slow reacting substance (SRS-A)

435. Rheumatoid factor is

(A) a complement component
(B) an HL-A-linked serum globulin
(C) a C-reactive protein
(D) denatured serum albumin
(E) IgM

436. The hinge region of an IgG heavy chain is located

(A) within the C_{H1} intrachain disulfide loop
(B) between C_{H1} and C_{H2}
(C) between C_{H3} and C_{H4}
(D) between C_{H4} and C_{H5}
(E) between V_H and C_{H1}

437. Which of the following statements about T cells is FALSE?

(A) The majority of circulating lymphocytes are T cells
(B) T cells of the mouse possess theta, TL, Ly, and H-2 alloantigens
(C) T cells are distributed in interfollicular areas of lymph nodes
(D) T cells proliferate in response to an antigen to which they have been primed
(E) T cells differentiate into antibody-secreting plasma cells

438. Which of the following subclasses of antibody is most abundant in serum?

(A) IgG-1
(B) IgG-2
(C) IgG-3
(D) IgG-4
(E) IgA-1

439. Which of the following antibodies sensitizes human mast cells for anaphylaxis?

(A) IgG-1
(B) IgG-3
(C) IgA-2
(D) IgM
(E) IgE

440. Genes which govern the ability of an animal to respond to a given antigen are called

(A) HL-A genes
(B) immune response genes
(C) immunoglobulin genes
(D) allogenes
(E) oncogenes

441. First and second locus antigens are separated in a histotype by a semicolon. Given the parental histotypes and that of one brother, which histotype may the propositus possess, assuming no crossover events?

Father   3, 25; 7, 12
Mother   1, 3; 8, 9
Brother 1, 25; 8, 12

(A) 1, 3; 7, 8
(B) 1, 3; 7, 12
(C) 3, 3; 7, 9
(D) 1, 25; 7, 12
(E) 3, 25; 7, 12

442. Many autoimmune and oncologic diseases show a statistical association with HL-A histotypes. The correlation is thought to occur because linkage disequilibrium exists between HL-A genes and other closely placed genes in the chromosome. Disease susceptibility, while loosely correlated with HL-A type, is felt to be more closely associated with another genetic locus, which is the

(A) Z gene for $alpha_1$-antitrypsin
(B) alpha immunoregulatory peptide gene
(C) immune response (Ir) genes
(D) immunoglobulin genes
(E) secretor/nonsecretor genes

443. The amounts of protein precipitated in a series of tubes containing a constant amount of antibody and varying amounts of antigen are presented below. In which tube is antigen-antibody equivalence obtained?

Tube	Antigen (mg)	Protein precipitated (mg)
(A) 1	0.02	1.1
(B) 2	0.08	2.1
(C) 3	0.32	3.1
(D) 4	1.0	3.7
(E) 5	2.0	2.9

444. When alleles of two or more linked genes are found together in a population more frequently than would be expected by random segregation, what phenomenon has occurred?

(A) Allotypic dominance
(B) Codominant expression
(C) Hysteresis
(D) Linkage disequilibrium
(E) Nondisjunction

445. The largest percentage of white cells in the peripheral blood is

(A) granulocytes
(B) macrophages
(C) null lymphocytes
(D) B lymphocytes
(E) T lymphocytes

446. Thrombocytopenic patients with aplastic anemia benefit from platelet transfusions during periods of severe platelet depression. Platelets may be rejected as ABO or HL-A incompatible. Given a patient's histotype of AB+ and HL-A 1, 3; 7, 12, which of the following donors would you prefer for platelet transfusions?

(A) O+   1, 3; 7, 12
(B) A+   3, 5; 7, 8
(C) O+   3, 5; 7, 8
(D) AB+ 2, –; 5, 13
(E) O–   1, –; 7, 13

447. What is the principal deterrent to successful transplantation of human hearts?

(A) High infection rate
(B) Inability to control rejection
(C) Psychosocial objections
(D) Insufficient surgical technique
(E) Unavailability of donor heart

448. What is the most commonly transplanted organ of humans?

(A) Bone marrow
(B) Kidney
(C) Liver
(D) Pancreas
(E) Skin

449. Which of the following cell surface alloantigens is NOT expressed by mouse T cells?

(A) H-2
(B) Ly
(C) PC
(D) Theta
(E) TL

450. An Ouchterlony gel diffusion plate shows the reaction of a polyspecific serum against several antigen preparations. As shown below, the center well in figure 1 contains polyspecific antiserum, first bleed; the center well in figure 2 contains polyspecific antiserum, second bleed; NS is normal saline. Cross reaction can be recognized between antigen X and antigen

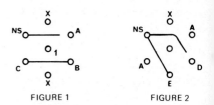

FIGURE 1   FIGURE 2

(A) A
(B) B
(C) C
(D) D
(E) E

451. Which of the following statements about transfer factor is FALSE?

(A) Delayed sensitivity begins one to seven days after injection of the cell extract and may last for more than one year
(B) It has a molecular weight of about 10,000
(C) It is stable on repeated freezing and thawing
(D) It is stable on trypsin treatment
(E) It is destroyed by DNase

Questions 452-454

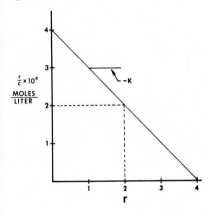

The Scatchard plot shown above represents the interaction of a hapten molecule with an immunoglobulin in an equilibrium dialysis apparatus.

$$K = \left(\frac{r}{n-r}\right)c \quad \text{or} \quad \frac{r}{c} = Kn - Kr,$$

where K is the intrinsic affinity constant, r is the number of hapten molecules bound per antibody molecule at c, the free concentration of hapten, and n is the antibody valence.

452. What is the affinity constant for this system?

(A) 1×10^{-4} moles/l
(B) 1×10^{4} moles/l
(C) 1×10^{4} l/mole
(D) -4×10^{-4} moles/l
(E) 16×10^{-4} moles/l

453. What is the antibody valence, n?

(A) 1
(B) 2
(C) 3
(D) 4
(E) 10

454. What is the antibody species used in this experiment?

(A) $F(ab')_2$
(B) Fab'
(C) secretory IgA
(D) IgE
(E) IgM

DIRECTIONS: Each question below contains four suggested answers of which **one** or **more** is correct. Choose the answer

A	if	1, 2, and 3	are	correct
B	if	1 and 3	are	correct
C	if	2 and 4	are	correct
D	if	4	is	correct
E	if	1, 2, 3, and 4	are	correct

455. Which of the following changes occur on removal of the bursa of Fabricius of a chicken?

(1) Circulating lymphocyte counts decrease markedly
(2) Germinal centers of the spleen atrophy
(3) Rejection of skin grafts is much slower
(4) Serum IgG levels fall

456. An Ouchterlony gel diffusion pattern is shown below of various fractions in the preparation of a membrane component X with antisera against the crude membrane. In the diagram, the center well contains antimembrane antiserum. NS is normal saline. Component X is found in

(1) Well 1
(2) Well 2
(3) Well 3
(4) Well 4

457. Which of the following physiologic disturbances may be observed in anaphylaxis?

(1) Edema
(2) Release of heparin
(3) Leukopenia
(4) Smooth muscle spasm

458. Passive immunity in newborn infants is a function of

(1) IgA
(2) IgD
(3) IgM
(4) IgG

459. Antibody production is dependent upon the

(1) amount of antigen administered
(2) time period over which the antigen is administered
(3) inherent antigenicity of the antigen
(4) route of administration

460. The Arthus reaction and the anaphylactic reaction differ because the Arthus reaction

(1) has no latent period for fixation of antibody to tissue cells
(2) may be delayed in development for several hours
(3) is not inhibited by antihistimines
(4) requires smaller amounts of antigen and antibody

461. Autoimmunity to sequestered protein is probably involved in

(1) thrombocytopenic purpura
(2) Goodpasture's syndrome
(3) rheumatic fever
(4) Hashimoto's thyroiditis

462. The graph below shows the sequential alteration in types of antibodies that occurs after an immunization. Curve A represents the total antibody production (the sum of curves B and C). The antibody class, i.e., IgG, IgA, IgM, etc., represented by curve C is

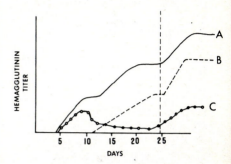

(1) estimated to have a molecular weight of 150,000
(2) composed of four peptide chains connected by disulfide links
(3) not produced in the neonate until approximately the third month of life
(4) the ABO isoagglutinin in humans

SUMMARY OF DIRECTIONS

A	B	C	D	E
1, 2, 3 only	1, 3 only	2, 4 only	4 only	All are correct

463. Which of the following statements about the precipitin curve shown below are true?

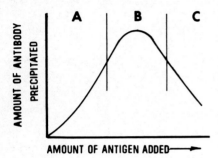

(1) In a multispecific system, "B" may have an excess of antigens and antibodies in the supernatant
(2) "A" and "C" have a similar excess of antibody in the supernatant
(3) In a monospecific system, "B" would contain only reacted antibody and antigen
(4) "A" has unreacted precipitable antigen in the supernatant

464. Carcinoembryonic antigens (CEA) are

(1) normal components of the fetal cell
(2) specific for colonic tumors
(3) not always found with extensive colonic malignancy
(4) unassociated with pancreatic tumors

465. In the mouse, B lymphocytes

(1) have cell surface immunoglobulins
(2) are found in a greater number than T lymphocytes in peripheral blood
(3) have a greater susceptibility to X-irradiation inactivation than T cells
(4) have theta antigen cell surface markers

466. Kappa and lambda light chains

(1) are identical at the Inv locus
(2) segregate genetically independently on different chromosomes
(3) are both found on one heavy chain dimer
(4) are precursors of Bence Jones proteins

467. J chains are found in which of the following immunoglobulins?

(1) IgG
(2) IgM
(3) IgE
(4) IgA

468. Which of the following pairs of IgG antigens and antibodies will form precipitin bands between wells in a gel diffusion experiment?

(1) Anti-Fab: heavy chains
(2) Anti-Fab: light chains
(3) Anti-Fc : heavy chains
(4) Anti-Fc : light chains

469. Which of the following hypotheses would sufficiently explain the non-precipitation of an antigen-antibody system?

(1) The antigen has a monovalent determinant
(2) The antigen has multiple, closely repeated determinants
(3) The antibody has been cleaved to divalent Fab' ligands
(4) The antibody has been cleaved to divalent $F(ab')_2$ ligands which cannot interact through cleaved Fc portions

470. B lymphocytes

(1) may differentiate into antibody-secreting cells
(2) have antigenic memory
(3) proliferate in vitro in response to specific antigen
(4) proliferate in vitro in response to lectin mitogens

471. Injury to vascular endothelium causes platelet adhesion to the injured site. The platelets adhere to

(1) connective tissue fibers
(2) endothelial cells
(3) ϵ-amino groups of lysine in collagen
(4) erythrocytes

472. Immune complex glomerulonephritis is seen in which of the following conditions?

(1) Chronic serum sickness
(2) Phenacetin ingestion
(3) Systemic lupus erythematosus
(4) Goodpasture's syndrome

473. Haptens

(1) are generally of low molecular weight (<1000)
(2) usually must be coupled covalently to a carrier to elicit an immune response
(3) are bound to antigen-binding sites of immunoglobulins which have been raised in response to them
(4) are coupled to endogenous proteins prior to sensitization, e.g., in poison ivy dermatitis

474. Which of the following procedures will yield a relatively pure population of T lymphocytes from peripheral blood?

(1) Sedimentation through a ficoll-hypaque density gradient after incubation and rosette formation with sheep erythrocytes
(2) Separation on a cell separator applying an electrostatic charge and field to drops with fluorescein tagged anti-IgG, and collection of the pool of non-tagged cells
(3) Passage through nylon fiber columns which bind IgG-bearing B cells and macrophages
(4) Treatment with anti-theta sera and incubation for 30 minutes with complement

SUMMARY OF DIRECTIONS

A	B	C	D	E
1, 2, 3 only	1, 3 only	2, 4 only	4 only	All are correct

475. Allotypes have been identified in which of the following molecules?

(1) Glucose 6-phosphate dehydrogenase
(2) Haptoglobin
(3) Hemoglobin
(4) HL-A histocompatibility antigen

476. Relative to the primary response, secondary and later booster responses to Dnp-ovalbumin in a given animal are associated with

(1) higher titers of antibody
(2) increases in affinity constant to Dnp-lysine
(3) increases in the avidity for Dnp-ovalbumin
(4) shifts in subclass or idiotype of antibody produced

DIRECTIONS: The groups of questions in this section consist of five lettered headings followed by several numbered items. For each numbered item choose the **one** lettered heading with which it is **most** closely associated. Each lettered heading may be used once, more than once, or not at all.

Questions 477-481
For each immunoglobulin, select its correct molecular weight.

(A) 150,000 (7 S)
(B) 180,000 (7 S)
(C) 200,000 (8 S)
(D) 170,000 or 400,000 (7 S or 11 S)
(E) 900,000 (19 S)

477. IgA, secretory D

478. IgD, serum B

479. IgE C

480. IgG A

481. IgM, serum E

Questions 482-486
For each disease, choose the humoral and cellular immune system description with which it is most likely to be associated.

	Humoral	Cellular
(A)	Normal	Normal
(B)	Deficient	Deficient
(C)	Deficient	Normal
(D)	Normal	Deficient
(E)	Elevated	Normal

482. Ataxia-telangiectasia B

483. Infantile X-linked agammaglobulinemia (Bruton's disease) C

484. Swiss type hypogammaglobulinemia B

485. Thymic hypoplasia (DiGeorge's syndrome) D

486. Wiskott-Aldrich syndrome B

Questions 487-490

For each technique or phenomenon select the investigators name with which it is associated.

(A) Coombs
(B) Danysz
(C) Farr
(D) Karush
(E) Ouchterlony

487. Precipitation of antigen-antibody complexes from a solution of high salt concentration, in which the uncomplexed antigen is soluble   C

488. Indirect agglutination of human red cells by rabbit anti-human IgG which recognizes human antibodies that are adsorbed onto the red cell but which are, themselves, not agglutinating   A

489. The serial addition over a period of time of several portions of antigen (toxin) to an antibody (antitoxin) yields a different equivalence point from that obtained when the entire amount of antigen is added to the same amount of antibody all at once   B

490. Antibodies too closely-spaced that repeat antigenic determinants, e.g., polysaccharides, are nonprecipitating because both arms of the antibodies will bind two determinants on one antigenic particle (monogamous bivalency)   D

Questions 491-493

Antigenic determinants on immunoglobulins are used to classify antibodies. For each classification of antibody below, select the determinant with which it is most likely to be associated.

(A) Determinant exposed after papain cleavage to a $F(ab')_2$ fragment
(B) Determinant of antibodies from one clone of cells, probably located close to the antigen binding site of the immunoglobulin
(C) Determinant recognized by alloantisera and inherited in a mendelian fashion
(D) Heavy chain determinant recognized by heterologous antisera
(E) Species-specific carbohydrate determinant on the heavy chain

491. Isotype   D

492. Allotype   C

493. Idiotype   B

Questions 494-498

For each diagnosis, choose the lettered electrophoretic profile shown below with which it is most likely to be associated.

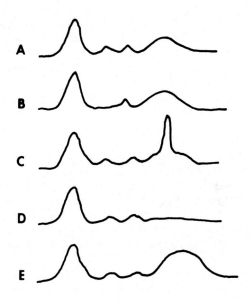

494. α_1-Antitrypsin deficiency

495. Multiple myeloma

496. Normal

497. Polyclonal hypergammaglobulinemia

498. Swiss agammaglobulinemia

Virolology

1. The answer is C. *(Davis, ed 2. pp 1016-1036.)* Viruses range in diameter from 20-300 nm. Icosahedral viral particles (or virions) have a 20-triangular faced protein shell (or capsid) surrounding a core of nucleic acid and protein. Viral forms vary in type of nucleic acid, degree of envelopment, and number of capsomers (the basic unit of the capsid).

2. The answer is C. *(Costlow, J Cell Physiol 82:411-420, 1973. Baserga, Life Sciences 15:1057-1071, 1974.)* G_0 is an experimentally demonstrable stage in the mitotic cycle, distinct from G_1, and is only attained by untransformed (normal) cells in culture and in vivo.

3. The answer is A. *(Nicolson, J Cell Biol 60:236-248, 1974.)* Concanavalin A is a plant lectin that specifically binds to α-D-mannopyranosyl and β-D-galactopyranosyl residues on the exterior cell surface. This lectin does not specifically bind elements of the microtubular system as do colchicine and vinblastine, or of the microfilamentar system as do colcemide and cytochalasin B.

4. The answer is D. *(Farber, Biochem J 122:189, 1971.)* DNA replication before mitosis occurs in G_0 and G_1. Mitosis preceding DNA replication occurs only in G_2. In a normal cell arrested in G_0, neither premature chromosome condensation or "unbalanced" synthesis occurs.

5. The answer is C. *(Rubin, Proc Natl Acad Sci 68:1461, 1971. Fujimoto, Proc Natl Acad Sci 68:1516-1519, 1971.)* The Lesch-Nyhan syndrome is caused by a deficiency of the enzyme hypoxanthine-guanine phosphoribosyltransferase. Since only cells that contain this enzyme incorporate the guanine analog azaguanine into nucleosides whose nucleic-acid products are lethal to the cells, a Lesch-Nyhan cell can survive in azaguanine-supplemented medium. The other cell types cited all contain normal amounts of this enzyme.

6. **The answer is A.** *(Tobey, J Cell Physiol 79:259-265, 1972.)* All the methods listed except bleomycin block, can halt cell cycles in a reversible fashion. Bleomycin, by contrast, blocks the cell cycle irreversibly in G_2.

7. **The answer is D.** *(Tobey, Cancer Res 31:46, 1971.)* Isoleucine deprivation blocks cells reversibly in G_1. All the other treatments listed produce blocks elsewhere in the cell cycle.

8. **The answer is B.** *(Vogel, J Cell Physiol 82:181-188, 1973. Malawista, Proc Natl Acad Sci 71:927-931, 1974.)* 3T3 mouse fibroblasts have been used as a cell-culture model system for examining the properties of untransformed (nonneoplastic) cells in culture. These cells are aneuploid, however, not diploid.

9. **The answer is C.** *(Davis, ed 2. p 1031.)* The envelope lipids are taken from pre-existing host cell membrane lipids. Viruses grown on different cell lines will show different lipid compositions.

10. **The answer is A.** *(Jawetz, ed 11. p 342.)* Many viruses agglutinate erythrocytes. This reaction may be inhibited by immune or convalescent serum which contains antibodies to the virus. Candidiasis is caused by the fungus *Candida albicans* which does not agglutinate erythrocytes. The four remaining diseases are caused by viruses that agglutinate red cells.

11. **The answer is D.** *(Davis, ed 2. pp 1183-1186.)* The common broad-spectrum antibiotics such as chloramphenicol, have no effect on viral infections. In addition to rifampin, FUDR, IUDR, and cytosine arabinoside, certain carboxypeptides, adamantanamine and substituted benzimidazole and guanidine have some proven therapeutic value.

12. **The answer is C.** *(Davis, ed 2. pp 1215-1216.)* In several viral diseases, the immune response manifests as a delayed hypersensitivity to the virus, thought to be caused by an allergic response to the virus or its products. X-irradiation or administration of anti-lymphocytic serum will suppress the immune response and thus the clinical signs and symptoms of lymphocytic choriomeningitis.

13. **The answer is B.** *(Bellanti, 1971. p 490.)* Certain combinations of live virus may result in one virus inhibiting the growth of the other so that immunization against the inhibited virus will not be successful. This interference appears to be mediated by the mechanism of interferon.

14. The answer is D. *(Bellanti, 1971. pp 279-281.)* Interferon is a protein produced by cells after viral infection, or in response to certain other agents, that enters uninfected cells. It causes them to produce a second protein which alters protein synthesis so that following infection, new viruses are not assembled.

15. The answer is E. *(Davis, ed 2. pp 1034-1036, 1308. Jawetz, ed 11. p 342.)* In the hemagglutination-inhibition test, the normal receptors on the virion, which attach to sites on the red blood cell membrane to cause the formation of aggregates of red cells, are inhibited by antiviral antibodies in immune or convalescent serum. Hemagglutination-inhibition is a convenient method of measuring antibodies to influenza virus as well as to rubella, mumps, measles, variola, vaccinia, various encephalitides, adenovirus and reovirus infections.

16. The answer is B. *(Davis, ed 2. p 1141.)* Reoviruses and picornaviruses are RNA-containing viruses. Adenoviruses are naked icosahedral structures without lipid envelopes. Herpesviruses contain a double-stranded DNA genome of $50\text{-}100 \times 10^6$ daltons, surrounded by a protein coat, in turn enclosed by a lipid envelope. The DNA genomes of poxvirus are very large, i.e., 160×10^6 daltons, and have lipid in the outer coat but no definite envelope.

17. The answer is E. *(Davis, ed 2. p 1281.)* Parainfluenza virus is a paramyxovirus. The other viruses are picornaviruses and are small ether-sensitive viruses with a single-stranded RNA genome. The nucleocapsid is naked.

18. The answer is A. *(Davis, ed 2. p 1383.)* Coxsackie is a picornavirus which is spread mainly through a fecal-oral route, while the others are arthropod-borne viruses. All except the coxsackievirus belong to the togaviruses, group B.

19. The answer is D. *(Davis, ed 2. pp 1141, 1240, 1336, 1368.)* Influenza is a myxovirus while RSV is a leukovirus. The other pairs are rhabdo-, herpes-, paramyxo-, and papova- viruses, respectively.

20. The answer is E. *(Jawetz, ed 11. pp 436-438.)* Verrucae or warts are caused by the papovavirus group. Herpesviruses (of which at least 25 varieties are known) contain double-stranded DNA. Other diseases linked to herpesviruses include labial and cervical carcinoma, lymphoma, keratoconjunctivitis, and meningoencephalitis.

21. The answer is C. *(Davis, ed 2. p 1331.)* Both mumps and measles are paramyxoviruses. They are enveloped and contain single-stranded RNA. Rabies is a rhabdo-, ectromelia a pox-, and zoster a herpes- virus. Hepatitis is as yet unclassified.

22. **The answer is A.** *(Davis, ed 2. pp 1400-1407.)* The reoviruses (*r*espiratory *e*nteric *o*rphan viruses) contain double-stranded RNA, are found in all mammals except whales, and are disease orphans.

23. **The answer is D.** *(Jawetz, ed 11. p 375.)* Echoviruses were discovered accidentally during studies on poliomyelitis. They were named *e*nteric *c*ytopathogenic *h*uman *o*rphan viruses because at the time they were unassociated with human disease. They are no longer, however, "orphans." They infect the human enteric tract and cause aseptic meningitis, febrile illnesses, and the common cold. They range in size from 24 to 30 nm in diameter and contain a core of RNA.

24. **The answer is C.** *(Davis, ed 2. pp 1419-1433.)* By definition, a tumor virus changes growth properties of cells. Tumor viruses are found in both RNA and DNA viral groups, and produce all types of cancer. Answers "D" and "E" are equivocal, although there is evidence that SV40 integrates its DNA into the host cell chromosome.

25. **The answer is A.** *(Davis, ed 2. pp 1298-1299.)* The coxsackieviruses (group A and B) produce a variety of illnesses, including aseptic meningitis, acute upper respiratory disease and paralytic disease simulating poliomyelitis. Twice the normal incidence of congenital heart lesions is found in infants whose mothers had coxsackievirus infections during the first trimester of pregnancy.

26. **The answer is A.** *(Jawetz, ed 11. p 289.)* All patients with exanthem subitum recover promptly and without any therapy. High fever usually persists for three to four days, and as the fever falls, pink maculopapules which persist for one to three days appear on the chest and trunk. There is no specific therapy.

27. **The answer is D.** *(Jawetz, ed 11. p 449.)* Common skin warts (verrucae) are caused by human wart virus (papilloma virus) belonging to the papova group (*pa*pilloma, *po*lyoma, *va*cuolating viruses). Human wart viruses do not grow in cultures or laboratory animals. The virus can be spread by direct or indirect contact between individuals, autoinoculation, or through scratching.

28. **The answer is B.** *(Davis, ed 2. pp 1299-1302.)* Echoviruses are found in the human gastrointestinal tract, have single-stranded RNA, have over 31 immunologic types, and are no longer disease orphans. In addition to causing aseptic meningitis, they cause paralysis, encephalitis, enteritis, and acute upper respiratory tract disease.

29. The answer is D. *(Jawetz, ed 11. pp 379-383.)* IgM levels are elevated in patients who have type A viral hepatitis. The abnormally high levels appear 3 to 4 days after the SGOT begins to increase. The normal incubation period for viral hepatitis A is only 15 to 50 days. Gamma globulin effectively prevent jaundice. The Australia antigen, or HB_s Ag antigen, is associated with hepatitis B.

30. The answer is E. *(Jawetz, ed 11. pp 285-287.)* Poliomyelitis is diagnosed by isolating the virus and/or demonstrating a rising antibody titer. Skin tests for trichinosis and leprosy exist but are of little value. Injection of inactivated hydatid fluid may lead to a diagnosis of echinococcosis (Casoni test). The most important test for tuberculosis is the PPD skin test.

31. The answer is E. *(Jawetz, ed 11. pp 373, 440.)* Smallpox causes generalized skin lesions. Herpangina, caused by group A coxsackieviruses, is associated with discrete oral vesicles; genital herpes with vesiculo-ulcerative lesions; zoster usually with a distribution of lesions over the area of innervation of the affected ganglion; and molluscum contagiosum with lesions distributed over the back, arms, and face.

32. The answer is C. *(Davis, ed 2. pp 1217-1218, 1261, 1264-1268.)* Smallpox virus infection is overwhelmingly virulent and acute. The other viruses mentioned may not cause clinically apparent disease although harbored in the host for years.

33. The answer is B. *(Davis, ed 2. pp 1212-1213.)* All the organisms listed, except poliovirus, remain primarily at the entry organ. They may, with time, erode to the blood or lymphatics and spread to distant sites, but this dissemination is not essential in producing the characteristic disease syndromes.

34. The answer is C. *(Jawetz, ed 11. p 368.)* Poliovirus is spread by fecal-oral transmission. Primary multiplication occurs at the implantation sites in the intestines or oropharynx. The virus is found in both the throat and stools before the onset of illness and is excreted in stools for several weeks after high antibody levels exist.

35. The answer is C. *(Briody, 1974. pp 606-608.)* Cytomegalovirus is species-specific. In human populations, infants are affected through intrauterine or early postnatal infection, but the mechanism of transmission for the general population remains unknown. LCM virus is carried by mice; *R. mooseri* by ticks; rabies by dogs and several other mammals; and *B. anthracis* by sheep.

36. The answer is A. *(Davis, ed 2. p 1373.)* There have been only one to three cases of rabies per year in the U.S. since 1960. On the other hand, there are still over 1,000 fatal cases reported annually worldwide, and in 1971, 4,392 cases of rabies were identified in animals in the U.S. alone.

37. The answer is C. *(Jawetz, ed 11. pp 445-446.)* The simian B virus, although rare in man, is extremely virulent and kills essentially all humans it infects. It causes acute encephalitis and myelitis with necrosis of the spleen, usually leading to death within ten days of onset. B virus is a latent infection in monkeys.

38. The answer is A. *(Davis, ed 2. pp 1246-1248.)* Varicella-herpes zoster virus causes a usually mild, self-limited illness in children. Infection of adults with circulating antibody may result, however, in a more severe illness with inflammatory involvement of the sensory ganglia of spinal or cranial nerves.

39. The answer is D. *(Burrows, ed 20. p 943.)* Mild disease resulting from infection with adenovirus, respiratory syncytial virus, influenza, or parainfluenza virus may be indistinguishable from the common cold. Nevertheless, the common cold appears to be caused most often by the rhinoviruses, RNA, ether-stable viruses.

40. The answer is B. *(Davis, ed 2. pp 1216, 1356-1357.)* Approximately 30 percent of the women who have clinical rubella during the first trimester of pregnancy give birth to babies with structural abnormalities.

41. The answer is B. *(Jawetz, ed 11. p 229.)* Condyloma acuminata is another name for venereal warts. It is not caused by *T. pallidum* but probably by a virus, and can be treated easily with podophyllin.

42. The answer is E. *(Davis, ed 2. p 1348.)* Live attenuated measles virus vaccine can effectively prevent measles and is the most effective control measure. It induces an antibody response in almost 100 percent of children inoculated, but it also produces a rash and/or fever in 10-25 percent of these cases. It does not have neurologic contraindications. Effective immunity may last up to eight years but it is still too early for complete evaluation of the period of protection.

43. The answer is D. *(Davis, ed 2. pp 1410-1413.)* HAA appears late (30-50 days after infection) in the incubation period of serum hepatitis, and may persist long after symptoms subside. HAA particles are known to contain protein but not nucleic acids although they have properties similar to viruses.

44. The answer is A. *(Horsfall, ed 4. pp 759-760.)* Mumps virus (one of the paramyxoviruses) rarely, if ever, affects the urinary tract. The testes and ovaries are fairly commonly involved; 20 percent of men over 13 who develop mumps will have orchitis. The mumps incubation period is usually around 20 days, and salivary adenitis, the major feature, lasts about one week.

45. The answer is D. *(Jawetz, ed 11. p 426.)* No reaction to vaccination is seen until day three or four in the fully susceptible person, when a papule surrounded by a narrow areola appears. The papule size increases until vesiculation occurs on day five or six. The maximum size of the vesicle is reached by day nine and the lesion then becomes pustular. Desiccation and regression follow, leaving a depressed pink scar. Repeat vaccination is indicated if this reaction is not produced.

46. The answer is C. *(Jawetz, ed 11, pp 416-417.)* Infants with rubella syndrome commonly have elevated IgM levels and low levels of IgG and IgA. Rubella infection during the first month of pregnancy produces abnormalities in approximately 80 percent of offspring; infection during the third month of gestation produces anomalies in only 15 percent of cases. Rubella virus does not actually destroy fetal cells, but rather involves a limited number of fetal cells and alters (slows) their growth rate.

47. The answer is E. *(Jawetz, ed 11. p 389.)* The definitive diagnosis of rabies is based on the finding of Negri bodies, which are cytoplasmic inclusions in the nerve cells of naturally infected patients or animals, or in the brains of animals inoculated in the laboratory. Negri bodies are not, however, found in all cases of rabies.

48. The answer is D. *(Jawetz, ed 11. pp 373, 393.)* Aseptic meningitis is characterized by a pleocytosis of mononuclear cells in the spinal fluid. The CSF is free of bacteria, contains normal glucose levels, and a slightly elevated protein content. Polymorphonuclear cells predominate during the first 24 hours; a shift to lymphocytes occurs thereafter and reaches high levels in lymphocytic choriomeningitis. Peripheral white cell counts are usually normal.

49. The answer is B. *(Jawetz, ed 11. p 422.)* The stages of smallpox exanthema are, in order: pre-eruptive, maculopapular, vesicular, pustular, and crusting.

50. The answer is D. *(Davis, ed 2. pp 1387-1388.)* Dengue fever (breakbone fever) is caused by a group B togavirus which is transmitted by mosquitoes. The clinical syndrome usually consists of a mild systemic disease characterized by severe joint and muscle pain, headache, fever, lymphadenopathy and a maculopapular rash. In some epidemics, hemorrhagic dengue fever, a more severe syndrome, may be prominent, resulting in shock and occasionally death.

51. The answer is D. *(Jawetz, ed 11. pp 346-347, 444.)* Infectious mononucleosis is characteristically accompanied by splenomegaly, the appearance of unique sheep cell hemagglutinins, an elevated peripheral white cell count, and the appearance of atypical leukocytes known as Downey cells. Patients may also develop antibodies to EB (Epstein-Barr) virus as measured by immunofluorescence of virus-bearing cells.

52. The answer is B. *(Harvey, ed 18. p 1116.)* The type A influenza virus infections are more serious than type B or C. Although transmission is from person-to-person, there are no known human carriers, and intraepidemic maintenance of the disease is a puzzle. Influenza has a fairly low case-fatality rate, but in pandemic form it does cause many deaths.

53. The answer is D. *(Davis, ed 2. pp 1289-1296.)* Ninety-eight percent of all poliovirus infections are mild and transient. The disease is transmitted from humans, disseminated by a viremia, and is rarely treated with gamma globulin.

54. The answer is E. *(Wintrobe, ed 7. p 931.)* Between 40 and 90 percent of common colds in adults are caused by rhinoviruses. The other four syndromes are also associated with infection by rhinoviruses but occur more frequently in young children than in adults.

55. The answer is A. *(Davis, ed 2. pp 1248, 1267.)* The eosinophilic inclusion bodies are intranuclear in chickenpox and cytoplasmic in smallpox (Guarnieri bodies). The inclusion bodies are composed of clumps of virus and viral antigens. Varicella characteristically is associated with giant cells.

56. The answer is E (all). *(Burrows, ed 20. pp 226-228.)* Robert Koch was the Nobel prize winner for medicine in 1909. He postulated that all the data given in the question choices were conditions a microorganism must fulfill to establish its etiologic relationship to a given disease.

57. The answer is D (4). *(Davis, ed 2. pp 1010, 1023-1025.)* Many groups of viruses contain an outer lipid envelope. While all viral genomes are comprised of a single type of nucleic acid, myxovirus double-stranded RNA is packaged as 10 separate molecules. Many viruses do carry specific enzymes, frequently involved in nucleic acid metabolism. Tumor viruses may package cellular RNA species.

58. The answer is E (all). *(Jawetz, ed 11. p 312.)* Interferon is a protein that alters cell metabolism to inhibit viral replication and is produced in all of the listed situations. It is species-specific but not virus-specific. It exists in at least two forms, one apparently preformed, one synthesized approximately 18 hours after appropriate stimulation.

59. The answer is B (1, 3). *(Jawetz, ed 11. p 293.)* The virion which is the complete infective virus particle is identical with the capsid and its nucleic acid core in adenoviruses, and picornaviruses. In more complex virions, such as herpesviruses, poxviruses, and myxoviruses, the virion consists of the nucleocapsid plus a surrounding envelope or complex coats.

60. The answer is A (1, 2, 3). *(Davis, ed 2. p 1207.)* Viral cytopathic effects are thought to include a change in the host cell's macromolecular synthesis and cell membrane structure. Viruses may produce cytopathic changes without forming infectious virions and without replicating infectious virus. A particular cytopathic effect is not necessarily associated with a specific virus.

61. The answer is A (1, 2, 3). *(Jawetz, ed 11. pp 379, 388, 408, 410.)* Rabiesvirus is inactivated in one hour at $50°C$ and in five minutes at $60°C$. Measles virus is destroyed at $56°C$ in one hour and mumps virus at the same temperature for 20 minutes. Hepatitis virus is highly resistant to heat and chemical agents. Its infectivity is destroyed in one hour at $180°C$.

62. The answer is A (1, 2, 3). *(Davis, ed 2. p 1190.)* A humoral antibody response can be elicited by viral products as well as by complete virions, and antibodies will react with internal as well as surface components of a virion. A cellular immune response can also be elicited by virus-specific proteins on the infected cell's surface membrane.

63. The answer is C (2, 4). *(Davis, ed 2. pp 1207-1208.)* Viral inclusion bodies may result from either the localized synthesis of virion sub-components or the storage of finished particles. They are often of crucial diagnostic importance, i.e., in distinguishing between smallpox and chickenpox. Viral inclusion bodies can be found in the nucleus or the cytoplasm of a cell, or in both, and they disrupt or kill the host cell.

64. **The answer is E (all).** *(Davis, ed 2. p 1206.)* Successfully virulent viruses are able to overcome host cell resistance factors and to multiply at temperatures found in a febrile host.

65. **The answer is E (all).** *(Davis, ed 2. p 1191.)* Virus-antibody complexes can be dissociated by changing pH, by sonic vibration, or by competition from inactivated virions. Neutralization is a function of the reaction between host cell, virion, and antibody. Identical virion-antibody mixtures will display divergent infectivity levels when assayed in different host cells.

66. **The answer is E (all).** *(Davis, ed 2. pp 1173-1181.)* In addition to all the qualities mentioned, interferon has a high specific activity. On a weight basis, it has more effect on viruses than do antibiotics on bacteria. Its value is limited, however, by its reversible action, its short period of effectiveness, and its inability to protect already infected cells.

67. **The answer is E (all).** *(Davis, ed 2. pp 1293, 1375, 1413-1414.)* Both forms of viral hepatitis are responsive to gamma globulin. Hyperimmune rabies antiserum prolongs the incubation period of the disease, allowing the patient more time to mount an immune response to the vaccine. Although not a primary form of treatment for poliomyelitis, man can be protected by passive immunization with pooled gamma globulin.

68. **The answer is E (all).** *(Davis, ed 2. pp 1274.)* N-methylisatin-β-thiosemicarbazone inhibits viral assembly, while vaccinia hyperimmune serum and transfer factor bolster the host defense mechanisms.

69. **The answer is E (all).** *(Jawetz, ed 11. pp 395-396.)* Slow viruses produce progressive neurologic disease and may have incubation periods of up to five years before their clinical manifestations become apparent. Progressive multifocal leukoencephalopathy (PML) and subacute sclerosing panencephalitis (SSPE) are also slow viruses, and other chronic diseases undoubtedly will someday prove to be of similar origin.

70. **The answer is E (all).** *(Jawetz, ed 11. p 322.)* Viruses may be transmitted by direct person-to-person contact through droplet or aerosol infection (influenza). Rabies is transmitted through a bite. Arboviruses use arthropods as vectors. Poliomyelitis is transmitted through the alimentary tract. Several viruses have multiple means of transmission which account for their variable epidemiologies.

71. The answer is A (1, 2, 3). *(Davis, ed 2. p 1389.)* WEE is caused by a group A togavirus. The natural reservoir for the infection is wild birds, and mosquitoes appear to be the primary vectors in the transmission to man and horses. Clinically similar encephalitides may be caused by a variety of related arboviruses including eastern equine encephalitis, St. Louis encephalitis and Japanese B encephalitis. In general, these encephalitides are characterized by sudden onset of headache, fever, and nausea, 4 to 21 days after inoculation.

72. The answer is A (1, 2, 3). *(Jawetz, ed 11. p 376.)* The rhinovirus subgroup of picornaviruses is composed of small, ether-insensitive viruses with an RNA genome. The virus enters via the upper respiratory tract and is the most common cause of colds in adults and children. Certain entero-, RS, corona-, influenza, parainfluenza, and adenoviruses also are causes of common colds.

73. The answer is E (all). *(Jawetz, ed 11. p 251. Paul, ed 3. pp 787-788.)* Primary atypical pneumonia is an acute, usually self-limited syndrome that includes pulmonary infiltration, cough, and fever. It is best diagnosed by x-ray. Infection ranges between asymptomatic and severe pneumonia and is caused by viruses, *M. pneumoniae*, and Q-fever rickettsiae.

74. The answer is D (4). *(Davis, ed 2. pp 1234, 1419.)* Adenovirus types 12 and 18 are able to cause tumors in neonatal hamsters, rats, and mice. In contrast, human cell infection is productive of infectious adenovirus progeny and the oncogenic potential of the organism is not expressed.

75. The answer is B (1, 3). *(Jawetz, ed 11. pp 419, 440.)* Smallpox and chickenpox are caused by DNA viruses. Measles (both rubella and rubeola) and yellow fever are caused by RNA-containing viruses.

76. The answer is B (1, 3). *(Davis, ed 2. pp 1378-1381.)* There are at least five large, distinguishable families of arthropod-borne viruses. They may or may not be enveloped and may contain either double- or single-stranded RNA. Physical and chemical studies have demonstrated a great heterogeneity among these viruses. Arboviruses cause disease in vertebrates but not in arthropod vectors.

77. The answer is D (4). *(Harvey, ed 18. pp 1152-1161.)* Infectious encephalitides are rarely produced by bacteria. They are practically always associated with fever and are essentially untreatable.

78. The answer is E (all). *(Jawetz, ed 11. pp 375-376.)* Echoviruses contain over 30 serotypes. In addition to the illnesses mentioned, they may cause aseptic meningitis, infantile diarrhea, and even vaginitis. Many of the echoviruses are still orphans. Enteroviruses produce transitory infections, primarily during the summer and autumn. The prevalence in children in poorer families is significantly higher.

79. The answer is A (1, 2, 3). *(Davis, ed 2. p 1299. Wintrobe, ed 7. p 946.)* In pleurodynia, chest pain and fever usually occur simultaneously and abruptly. Pain is severe and aggravated by movement. It is accompanied by abdominal muscle spasms in about 50 percent of cases. The illness is self-limited and although recovery is complete, relapses are common. Orchitis occurs in approximately 4 percent of cases during relapse.

80. The answer is C (2, 4). *(Davis, ed 2. pp 1362-1366.)* Coronaviruses were discovered in 1965, in the search for the etiologic agent of the common cold. Their name originates from their peculiar club-shaped surface projections that make them resemble solar coronas. The virion is known to contain RNA, but other elements of its structure are uncertain. It is thought to be a major agent of the common cold, especially in older children and adults.

81. The answer is C (2, 4). *(Davis, ed 2. pp 1222-1223, 1232-1234, 1303.)* Adenoviruses usually cause self-limited or inapparent infections. Their clinical importance is largely restricted to respiratory disease among military personnel and epidemic keratoconjunctivitis. They are composed of a single molecule of double-stranded DNA and protein. They permit replication to occur in the defective adeno-associated viruses.

82. The answer is C (2, 4). *(Jawetz, ed 11. pp 388-390. Wintrobe, ed 7. pp 956-958.)* Rabiesvirus has a single antigenic type, and a fatality rate of almost 100 percent. Most animals can transmit the virus for only a few days (a dog for five) before they become ill. The bat is a notable exception to this rule. The incubation period in man varies from 2 to 16 weeks or longer but usually lasts 2 to 3 weeks.

83. The answer is E (all). *(Davis, ed 2. pp 1250-1251.)* Cytomegalovirus infection is common but only rarely causes clinically apparent disease. Characteristic lesions are found in up to 10 percent of stillborn babies but are not necessarily the cause of death. Children and adults with immunosuppressive problems are susceptible to active disease. Control is not yet available.

84. The answer is C (2, 4). *(Jawetz, ed 11. p 416.)* Rubella infection during pregnancy may involve the placenta and fetus. The virus may retard the growth of fetal cells. The earlier in pregnancy that the infection occurs, the higher the percentage of extensive abnormal involvement of the newborn. Severe abnormalities can include congenital heart disease, interstitial pneumonitis, growth retardation, eye defects, neurosensory deafness, and cerebral palsy.

85. The answer is E (all). *(Wintrobe, ed 7. pp 969-971.)* Varicella-zoster virus is readily diagnosed by examining the cells from skin scrapings of the vesicular lesions. Fifteen percent of adults with varicella develop pneumonia. Encephalomyelitis is a rare complication in children. Generalized zoster occurs in five percent of affected patients and in the presence of severe underlying disease may lead to death.

86. The answer is A (1, 2, 3). *(Burrows, ed 20, pp 876-877.)* Herpesviruses are double-stranded DNA-containing, ether-sensitive viruses. At least 25 viruses in this grouping have been identified. Herpes simplex types 1 and 2, varicella-zoster, EB, and cytomegalovirus infect man.

87. The answer is E (all). *(Burrows, ed 20. pp 882-883.)* Fifty to eighty percent of patients with infectious mononucleosis develop an increased titer of heterophil antibodies that can be demonstrated by agglutination of sheep erythrocytes. Titers ranging from 1:10-1:40 are negative: titers of 1:160 or more are positive. Lymphadenopathy and atypical lymphocytes are found in infectious mononucleosis and the Epstein-Barr virus is thought to be the etiologic agent.

88. The answer is A (1, 2, 3). *(Davis, ed 2. pp 1308-1311, 1323.)* The hemagglutinin and neuraminidase antigens are extremely useful in diagnosis and quantitation of influenza virus. These viruses are found in horses, pigs, and chickens and often have antigenic properties similar to human strains. Influenza viruses are thought to inhibit phagocytosis of bacteria and in this way contribute to the severity of bacterial respiratory infections.

89. The answer is B (1, 3). *(Jawetz, ed 11. pp 413-414.)* Parainfluenza viruses form a subgroup of paramyxoviruses, and are recognized by their ability to lyse, as well as agglutinate, erthrocytes. Parainfluenza 2 virus appears to be the main agent causing croup in children. Antigenically, it is unrelated to all the other paramyxoviruses except for mumps virus. Parainfluenza 4 is not known to cause any human illness.

90. The answer is E (all). *(Jawetz, ed 11. p 374.)* Coxsackieviruses can also cause aseptic meningitis, hand-foot-and-mouth disease, and colds. They are becoming increasingly well known as a primary cause of myocarditis in adults as well as in children. Neonatal disease due to coxsackievirus group B is characterized by lethargy, fever, vomiting, and, in some cases, by initial manifestations of anorexia and diarrhea.

91. The answer is C (2, 4). *(Jawetz, ed 11. p 422.)* Guarnieri bodies are cytoplasmic inclusions characteristically found in cells infected with variola major. Variola virus causes a transient viremia that is followed by infection of reticuloendothelial cells throughout the body. A secondary phase of multiplication within reticuloendothelial cells leads to a second, more intense, viremia and clinical disease.

92. The answer is A (1, 2, 3). *(Davis, ed 2. pp 1346-1347.)* Measles virus has been isolated from patients with giant cell pneumonia. This virus has also been implicated, on the basis of high antibody titers and other data, in the pathogenesis of the slow viral infection SSPE. The incidence of encephalomyelitis associated with measles is approximately 1 in 10,000 cases.

93. The answer is B (1, 3). *(Davis, ed 2. p 1275.)* Molluscum contagiosum virus causes a rare skin disease found primarily in children and young adults. The virus stimulates cell division in uninfected neighboring cells and DNA synthesis ceases in the infected cells. The chronic lesion is restricted to the epithelium of the skin of the back, face, arms, legs, and genitals. Electron microscopy shows virions that are identical to other poxviruses.

94. The answer is E (all). *(Jawetz, ed 11. pp 430-435.)* The adenovirus group contains more than 30 antigenic types. In addition to the characteristics mentioned, they are ether-resistant, double-stranded DNA viruses.

95. The answer is D (4). *(Jawetz, ed 11. p 438.)* Acute herpetic gingivostomatitis is the most common clinical disease due to primary infections with type 1 herpesvirus. It occurs most frequently in small children and causes extensive lesions of the mucous membranes of the oral cavity, local lymphadenopathy, and fever.

96. The answer is E (all). *(Jawetz, ed 11. p 440.)* Both varicella (chickenpox) and zoster (shingles) are caused by the same virus. Varicella is easily transmitted by vesicular fluid, although zoster contact infection is rare. Varicella is the acute disease which follows primary infection, while zoster represents reactivation of a latent infection. The virus propagates in cultures of human embryonic tissue, producing eosinophilic intranuclear inclusions.

97. The answer is D (4). *(Briody, 1971. pp 603-604.)* The first three choices are old wives tales without any scientific basis. Parotid swelling can be unilateral but natural mumps infection confers solid immunity after a single infection. (Other viruses and bacteria do cause parotitis!) Sterility from mumps orchitis is rare; only 20 percent of males over the age of 13 even develop orchitis. The virus is maintained exclusively in human populations. The mumps vaccine is a live attenuated virus vaccine derived from chick embryo tissue culture.

98. The answer is B (1, 3). *(Wintrobe, ed 7. pp 450-451.)* Poliovirus occurs naturally solely in man, but most strains will infect monkeys and chimpanzees. It is transmitted by the oral-fecal route, and can remain viable in sewage for up to four months. There are three antigenically distinct, non-cross reacting types.

99. The answer is B (1, 3). *(Davis, ed 2. pp 1315-1317.)* Influenza A viruses have undergone three major antigenic shifts since the 1933 pandemic, and each shift has found a large part of the population susceptible. This antigenic variation, or drift, creates serious problems in developing effective vaccines. Smaller, minor antigenic changes, occurring every two to three years, have had lesser impact due to cross-reactivity of the neutralizing antibodies. Variations in influenza B viruses have been less marked, less frequent, and have all been subject to immune cross-reactivity.

100. The answer is B (1, 3). *(Burrows, ed 20. pp 962-964. Jawetz, ed 11. p 355.)* The reservoir of St. Louis encephalitis virus is wild birds but the disease is transmitted by mosquitoes. The incidence is over six times as high in adults as in children and in the 1966 epidemic, all reported deaths occurred in adults 45 years of age or older.

101. The answer is A (1, 2, 3). *(Burrows, ed 20. pp 916-918. Wintrobe, ed 7. pp 957, 1719.)* Chiropteran rabies or bat rabies may differ from canine strains and produce an ascending myelitis and spreading paralysis resembling the Landry-Guillain-Barré syndrome. It is interesting to note that antirabies inoculations have been reported to precede the onset of Landry-Guillain-Barré syndrome. The incubation period of human rabies is from a minimum of two weeks up to a year. Rabies is an ether-sensitive RNA virus which forms Negri bodies.

102. The answer is D (4). *(Davis, ed 2. pp 1242-1245.)* Herpes simplex virus infection initially occurs through a break in the skin or mucous membranes and is often inapparent. Latent infection often persists at the initial site despite high antibody titers. Recurrent disease can be triggered by temperature change, emotional factors, and hormones. Type 1 herpes simplex virus is usually associated with ocular and oral lesions: type 2 is usually associated with genital and anal lesions.

103. The answer is E (all). *(Davis, ed 2. p 1216.)* In 1941, Gregg firmly linked rubella infection during pregnancy with congenital anomalies. Rubella remains the major viral cause of fetal death. Cytomegalovirus may cause microcephaly; herpesvirus may cause central nervous system pathology; coxsackievirus may cause cardiac lesions.

104. The answer is D (4). *(Briody, 1971. pp 599-601.)* All of Koch's postulates have been verified for the relationship between infectious mononucleosis and EB virus. However, the relationship between EB virus and Burkitt's lymphoma, sarcoid, systemic lupus erythematosus (SLE), or leprosy is not yet clear. The disease is most common in young adults (15-20 years of age) and is very rare in young children. There is no specific treatment. Heterophil antibody is helpful in diagnosis.

105. The answer is E (all). *(Wintrobe, ed 7. p 964.)* Rubella infection can be easily confused with mononucleosis or mild enteroviral infections. It is most frequent in children five to nine years of age and occurs epidemically every six to nine years.

106. The answer is A (1, 2, 3). *(Wintrobe, ed 7. pp 961-963.)* Inactivated vaccine is contraindicated in measles because it may cause a severe, atypical form of the disease upon subsequent exposure. Rash progressing from feet to head, pneumonia, and edema are characteristic of this atypical form of measles. Live measles vaccine is highly effective, but should not be given to pregnant women, tuberculous patients, or patients receiving immunosuppresive therapy. Measles is not associated with orchitis.

107. The answer is E (all). *(Jawetz, ed 11. pp 478-479.)* Epstein-Barr (EB) virus, a member of the herpes group, has been associated with infectious mononucleosis, nasopharyngeal carcinoma and Burkitt's lymphoma. It is not yet clear whether EB virus is the etiologic agent of the malignancies or merely a passenger virus. Herpesvirus type 2 antibodies have been found in association with carcinoma of the cervix but again it is not known whether this association is etiologic. In at least one cervical cancer biopsy, herpesvirus DNA and mRNA were reported.

108-112. The answers are: 108-C, 109-D, 110-D, 111-B, 112-A. *(Jawetz, ed 11. p 323.)* In developed countries, it is recommended that the general population standardly be immunized against measles, rubella, mumps, and poliomyelitis; live attenuated virus vaccines made from a variety of tissue cultures are used. Under the appropriate circumstances, inactivated virus vaccines are given for rabies and EEE, and activated virus vaccine made from lymph or chorioallantois is given for smallpox.

Bacteriology

113. The answer is C. *(Jawetz, ed 11. pp 12-15.)* It is the cell wall of gram-positive bacteria that acts as a barrier to the extraction of crystal violet-iodine complex by alcohol. This property is the basis of the Gram stain. Organisms that retain the crystal violet-iodine complex are gram-positive: organisms that decolorize are considered gram-negative. It is the ability of the gram-negative cell wall to hinder penetration by large molecules that accounts for a relative resistance to antibiotics.

114. The answer is E. *(Davis, ed 2. p 523.)* In the presence of specific antibody and complement, red blood corpuscles and most gram-negative organisms undergo lysis. However, for poorly understood reasons, gram-positive organisms, i.e., streptococci and mycobacteria, are not lysed under these conditions.

115. The answer is C. *(Davis, ed 2. p 34.)* *Pasteurella* is a gram-negative genus. All of the other choices are gram-positive. Species of pasteurellae are responsible for plague (*P. pestis*) and tularemia (*P. tularensis*).

116. The answer is A. *(Jawetz, ed 11. pp 230-231.)* Serologic tests for syphilis fall into two groups: tests for the presence of reagin (VDRL and Wassermann); and tests for the presence of specific antitreponemal antibodies (fluorescent antibody test, i.e., FTA-ABS, and TPI). The Frei test is a skin test used in the diagnosis of lymphogranuloma venereum.

117. The answer is B. *(Jawetz, ed 11. pp 180, 285.)* The Dick test can be used to show susceptibility to the beta-hemolytic streptococcal erythrogenic toxin that causes the rash of scarlet fever. It is no longer, however, widely used. Tuberculosis is associated with the PPD-S test; lymphogranuloma venereum with the Frei test; and sarcoidosis with the Kveim test.

118. The answer is C. *(Davis, ed 2. p 820.)* *Bacillus anthracis* is an unusually large gram-positive organism, up to 8 microns in length and 1.5 microns in width. It causes anthrax in sheep and other animals but only rarely is pathogenic for man. When it does occur in man, it usually manifests as a malignant pustule resulting from a contaminated scratch or superficial wound. Another form is woolsorters' disease.

119. The answer is C. *(Jawetz, ed 11. p 124.)* Kanamycin is effective in treatment of severe bacteremia caused by gram-negative enteric organisms. It can be both ototoxic and nephrotoxic. Alternative antibiotic agents are ampicillin and cephalothin.

120. The answer is C. *(Davis, ed 2. pp 45-46.)* *Aerobacter* and certain enterobacteriaceae and *Bacillus* ferment pyruvate to form butylene glycol. On exposure to air, this compound is oxidized to acetoin. The presence of this compound can be readily determined by the Voges-Proskauer test. It is of value in differentiating between *E. coli* and *Aerobacter*.

121. The answer is E. *(Jawetz, ed 11. p 124.)* Penicillin is the drug of choice for many infections including gonorrhea, meningococcal meningitis, anthrax and leptospirosis. *Mycoplasma* is treated best with tetracycline or erythromycin.

122. The answer is B. *(Wintrobe, ed 7. pp 872-873.)* Dapsone is at present considered to be the drug of choice for treating leprosy. A maintenance dose of 50 mg per day in adults, administered over several months, will cause the basic disease to cease. However, leptomatous bacilli will persist in the host for many years and dapsone should be given for three to ten years. Recent information has shown that rifampin may be the future drug of choice for leprosy.

123. The answer is B. *(Davis, ed 2. pp 885-886.)* The original Wassermann test was a complement-fixation test. However, it was found that false-positive reactions to it occurred in a variety of other conditions including malaria, leprosy, lupus erythematosus and polyarteritis nodosa. Variations of the Wassermann test based on flocculation reactions have now been developed in the search for a more specific test.

124. The answer is B. *(Burrows, ed 20. p 643.)* Löffler's medium is used to culture diphtheria bacilli. It is especially useful in throat cultures as the medium fails to support the growth of other common pharyngeal organisms (pneumococci, streptococci). Thayer-Martin medium is used for *N. gonorrhoeae*.

125. The answer is C. *(Davis, ed 2. p 695.)* The quellung reaction is used for quick identification of pneumococci. They are mixed with a specific antipolysaccharide on a slide and their capsules can be seen to swell markedly.

126. The answer is B. *(Jawetz, ed 11. p 198.)* In unimmunized individuals diphtheria toxin produces an inflammatory reaction over the course of several days: in persons immune to diphtheria, circulating antibodies prevent this reaction. A minority of patients are hypersensitive to extraneous factors in the toxin/toxoid and develop a pseudoreaction consisting of inflammations that simultaneously disappear within three days in both arms, thus demonstrating immunity. An initial reaction in both arms that subsides quickly only at the toxoid site demonstrates hypersensitivity and susceptibility.

127. The answer is D. *(Jawetz, ed 11. pp 124, 129.)* Gentamicin and polymyxin are drugs of first choice against *Pseudomonas aeruginosa*. The polymyxins are polypeptide antibiotics active against a variety of gram-negative rods. They act by attacking the cellular membrane and causing leakage of the cellular contents. Their inherent CNS toxicity is largely reversible.

128. The answer is B. *(Jawetz, ed 11. p 180.)* An unknown rash can be demonstrated to be the rash of scarlet fever by the Schultz-Charlton reaction. Antibody to erythrogenic toxin is injected directly into the rash. If the rash fades or disappears the diagnosis of scarlet fever can be made with certainty.

129. The answer is C. *(Jawetz, ed 11. p 124.)* The correct drugs of choice are as follows: *T. pallidum*, syphilis, penicillin; *P. aeruginosa*, urinary tract infections, gentamicin; *P. mirabilis*, urinary tract infections, ampicillin; *A. israelii*, actinomycosis, penicillin; *M. leprae*, leprosy, sulfones.

130. The answer is E. *(Jawetz, ed 11. p 180.)* The Dick test demonstrates immunity to the toxin produced by certain streptococci which cause scarlet fever. Individuals immune to this toxin can still become infected with streptococci but will not develop the skin rash characteristic of scarlet fever. The Kline test, Kahn test, and Kolmer test are used in the diagnosis of syphilis.

131. The answer is E. *(Davis, ed 7. pp 815, 892, 1005.)* *Trichophyton rubrum* is a dermatophyte, or a skin fungi, that causes "athlete's foot."

132. The answer is C. *(Davis, ed 2. pp 635-637.)* The exotoxins of tetanus and botulinus act directly on the nervous system. Shiga toxin acts on the smaller cerebral blood vessels and diphtheria toxin on the body cells in general to produce CNS damage. Rabiesvirus does not produce a toxin. The CNS symptoms are produced by viral multiplication which causes a specific cytoplasmic inclusion, the Negri body, to develop in infected nerve cells.

133. The answer is B. *(Wintrobe, ed 7. p 58.)* Inapparent infections of most of the organisms mentioned may present as fever of obscure origin. *Clostridium novyi*, however, causes gas gangrene, a rapidly progressive infection of contaminated wounds as of the postpartum uterus.

134. The answer is C. *(Jawetz, ed 11. p 175.)* Typically, staphylococci are gram-positive spherical cells found in irregular grape-like masses. They are nonmotile and do not form spores. Pathogenic strains often produce a variety of enzymes and toxins including coagulase, hemolysin, leukocidin, and enterotoxin.

135. The answer is D. *(Davis, ed 2. p 725.)* Subacute bacterial endocarditis is an insidious infection that occurs on heart valves previously damaged by disease. The most common causative agents are α-streptococci (viridans streptococci). In contrast, acute bacterial endocarditis is a rapidly progressive infection that occurs on undamaged valves and may be caused by staphylococci, enterococci, and pneumococci.

136. The answer is A. *(Davis, ed 2. pp 758-759, 776-777.)* Both shigellae and salmonellae are gram-negative enteric bacilli that ferment mannitol. Both are methyl red positive, Voges-Proskauer and urease negative. Shigellae are distinguished by their lack of motility.

137. The answer is D. *(Jawetz, ed 11. pp 186-187.)* Pathogenic neisseriae (*N. meningitidis, N. gonorrhoeae*) will not grow on plain agar. They grow best on blood-enriched plates in the presence of 10% CO_2. *N. meningitidis* will ferment maltose and must be, therefore, strain A: *N. gonorrhoeae* will not and is, therefore, strain B. Strain C could be either *N. catarrhalis* or *N. flavescens*. *N. sicca* ferments sucrose, maltose, and dextrose, and grows on plain agar.

138. The answer is B. *(Jawetz, ed 11. p 185.)* The clinical syndrome described in the question is classic for pneumococcal pneumonia. Pneumonia is frequently preceded by an upper respiratory infection. The treatment of choice is penicillin G. With proper antimicrobial therapy, the patient can be afebrile within 48 hours and consolidation of the lungs can be avoided.

139. The answer is A. *(Davis, ed 2. p 784.)* *P. aeruginosa* may cause severe and potentially fatal infections in patients with extensive burns and may also be responsible for urinary tract infections, septicemia, abscesses, and meningitis. It flourishes particulary well in patients being treated with corticosteroids or antibiotics. While there may be little to differentiate *Pseudomonas* from other gram-negative infections, Wood's ultraviolet light will usually identify it in wounds and burns and most strains produce a characteristic blue-green pigment pyocyanin.

140. The answer is E. *(Wintrobe, ed 7. p 792.)* Strains of *E. coli* although part of the normal intestinal flora become pathologic when they invade other organ systems. Over 50 percent of *E. coli* infections begin in the urinary tract and 75 percent of urinary tract infections are caused by *E. coli*. These organisms can produce infection in any area of the body.

141. The answer is A. *(Jawetz, ed 11. p 176.)* Certain strains of staphylococci elaborate an enterotoxin that is frequently responsible for food poisoning. Typically, the toxin is produced when staphylococci grow on foods rich in carbohydrates. The toxin is preformed, i.e., present in the food when it is consumed. The resulting gastroenteritis is not dependent upon bacterial multiplication in the GI tract but only on the toxin.

142. The answer is C. *(Davis, ed 2. pp 708-724.)* Suppurative ("pus producing") streptococcal disease refers to the group of clinical syndromes produced by streptococci as a direct result of bacterial multiplication and exotoxin production. The syndromes include otitis media, erysipelas, and pharyngitis. The antiphagocytic properties of the capsule and cell wall, as determined by the presence of hyaluronic acid and the M protein, are important pathogenic factors.

143. The answer is C. *(Jawetz, ed 11. p 196.)* Corynebacteria may be recognized microscopically by Babes-Ernst bodies, metachromatic granules made visible by aniline staining that give the rods a beaded appearance. Also characteristic of corynebacteria are their club-shaped appearance and tendency to form "Chinese letters."

144. The answer is C. *(Wintrobe, ed 7. p 767.)* When repeated attacks of the same type of pneumococcal pneumonia occur in a patient, dysgammaglobulinemia, especially multiple myeloma, should be suspected. Recurrent infection is probably due to the inability of the host to produce anticapsular antibody which would increase the phagocytosis of the bacteria in the lungs. Impaired pulmonary function (certain forms of anesthesia) and alcoholic intoxication also tend to increase occurrences of pneumococcal pneumonia via a delay in the appearance of polymorphonuclear leukocytes.

145. The answer is C. *(Wintrobe, ed 7. pp 789-790.)* Previously asymptomatic infections of gonorrhea frequently become manifest during menstruation or pregnancy. The onset of clinical gonococcal infection is characterized by fever, chills, and polyarthralgia. These symptoms may be followed by acute arthritis in one or more joints, acute salpingitis, and sterility.

146. The answer is D. *(Davis, ed 2. p 682.)* *Corynebacterium diphtheriae* is the causative agent of diphtheria. It is a gram-positive rod with club-shaped ends. On staining, the bacilli characteristically form palisades resembling Chinese letters. Other corynebacteria, such as *C. xerosis* and *C. pseudodiphtheriticum* (*C. hofmannii*), while frequent inhabitants of man, rarely produce disease.

147. The answer is D. *(Davis, ed 2. pp 946-948.)* Granulomatosis infantiseptica (perinatal listeric septicemia) is associated with an often asymptomatic, low-grade, intrauterine infection; is characterized by necrosis of the meninges and liver; and causes a high mortality rate in the newborn. Intrauterine infection may also result in stillbirth or abortion. *Listeria monocytogenes* is a short gram-positive, nonspore-forming rod. In adults it may cause meningitis or meningoencephalitis.

148. The answer is E. *(Jawetz, ed 11. pp 175-176.)* Staphylococci are gram-positive, nonspore-forming cocci that ferment many carbohydrates. Clinically, their antibiotic resistance poses major problems. Many strains produce β-lactamase (penicillinase) which destroys penicillins by opening the lactam ring. Drug resistance, mediated by plasmids, may be transferred by transduction.

149. The answer is C. *(Harvey, ed 18. p 1123.)* The etiologic agent of pneumonia varies with the patient's age and clinical situation. Diplococci are the most frequent causative organisms in adults. Mycoplasmal pneumonia is common among young adults and military recruits. Patients with cardiopulmonary disease are prone to infection with influenza virus and alcoholics and diabetics are often infected with *Klebsiella*.

150. The answer is B. *(Jawetz, ed 11. pp 221, 223.)* *Pasteurella (Francisella) tularensis* is harbored in wild rodents and can be transmitted to man by arthropod bites, by handling or eating infected animals, or via the respiratory tract. Initial clinical findings usually include lesions at the site of entry and adenopathy. Necrotizing granulomatous nodules form in several organs and untreated the disease progresses to septicemia, pneumonia, and death.

151. The answer is C. *(Davis, ed 2. pp 695-696, 705.)* Diplococci and streptococci are both gram-positive cocci. While their morphology may give some clue as to their identity, both diplococci and streptococci may form short chains. Differentiation is aided by the quellung reaction. In the presence of type-specific antibody, the capsules of pneumococci will swell markedly.

152. The answer is B. *(Jawetz, ed 11. pp 233, 259-260.)* *Actinomyces israelii* is a gram-positive organism which despite its fungal-like appearance, is a eubacteria. It characteristically produces abscesses of the face and neck that have a tendency to drain spontaneously and form chronic sinus tracts. Diagnosis may be made by finding typical sulfur granules in the pus or by culture on thioglycollate medium. *A. bovis* causes "lumpy jaw" in cattle.

153. The answer is B. *(Davis, ed 2. p 795. Wintrobe, ed 7. pp 814, 1801.)* Except during a meningococcal epidemic, *H. influenzae* is the most common cause of bacterial meningitis in children. Most cases are secondary to respiratory tract infections or otitis media. *H. influenzae, N. meningitidis,* and *D. pneumoniae* account for 80 to 90 percent of cases of bacterial meningitis.

154. The answer is E. *(Jawetz, ed 11. p 181.)* Puerperal fever is an infection of the uterus which may follow childbirth or abortion. It is commonly caused by streptococci, staphylococci, or *E. coli.* Rarely, clostridia may be the causative agent especially following criminal abortions.

155. The answer is A. *(Jawetz, ed 11. p 177.)* *Staphylococcus aureus* is the species of *Staphylococcus* most often associated with human disease. The species is hemolytic, pigmented, coagulase-positive, and ferments mannitol.

156. The answer is D. *(Jawetz, ed 11. p 192.)* *Clostridium botulinum* grown on food produces a potent neurotoxin which when ingested by humans produces diplopia, dysphagia, respiratory paralysis, and speech difficulties. The toxin is thought to act by blocking acetylcholine action at neuromuscular junctions. *Cl. botulinum* infection in man is extremely rare.

157. The answer is E. *(Davis, ed 2. pp 697-698. Jawetz, ed 11. p 185.)* The virulence of pneumococci is dependent upon the presence of a capsule. The capsular polysaccharides inhibit phagocytosis and destruction of the organism. In serum that contains specific anticapsular antibodies, the protective function is lost. Pneumococci may be typed on the basis of their polysaccharides.

158. The answer is E. *(Wintrobe, ed 7. pp 1171-1173.)* Rheumatic fever follows group A β-hemolytic streptococcal infections. Eighty percent of these infections will produce an elevated antistreptolysin O titer. The diagnosis can be made when two major Jones' criteria or one major and two minor are met. The disease occurs most commonly in the 5 to 17-year-old age group.

159. The answer is D. *(Davis, ed 2. p 768.)* Urine is normally sterile. However, in the process of voiding or collection of a urine sample contamination may occur. If the bacterial count is less than 1×10^4, infection is unlikely; if it is greater than 1×10^5, *E. coli.* infection is highly probable.

160. The answer is D. *(Wintrobe, ed 7. p 1621.)* Many types of infection are common in the sickle-cell patient including osteomyelitis. For unknown reasons, *Salmonella* is frequently implicated in these infections. In normal patients, osteomyelitis is most often caused by *Staphylococcus*.

161. The answer is A. *(Jawetz, ed 11. p 252.)* Oroya fever, a disease found only in the Andes Mts. of Peru, Colombia and Ecuador, is caused by *Bartonella bacilliformis*. The infection is characterized by severe anemia, hepatosplenomegaly, and hemorrhage. The same organism may cause a benign skin infection (verruga peruana).

162. The answer is E. *(Jawetz, ed 11. p 193.)* *Clostridium tetani*, an anaerobic, gram-positive rod, is the causative organism of tetanus. It is often found in soil and animal feces and produces a localized infection in contaminated wounds, burns, or surgical incisions. *C. tetani* produces a powerful neurotoxin that causes violent tonic contractions of voluntary muscles. The common name for tetanus "lockjaw" derives from the intense spasms produced in masseter muscles.

163. The answer is B. *(Jawetz, ed 11. p 197.)* Diphtheria produced by *C. diphtheriae* usually begins as a pharyngitis associated with "pseudomembrane" formation and lymphadenopathy. The growing organisms produce a potent exotoxin which is absorbed in mucous membranes and causes remote damage to the liver, kidneys, and heart. While *C. diphtheriae* may infect the skin, it rarely invades the blood stream and never actively invades deep tissue.

164. The answer is B. *(Jawetz, ed 11. p 181.)* Viridans streptococci can produce α-hemolysis (green hemolysis) on blood agar plate but not β-hemolysis. They are normal inhabitants of the oral flora and are frequently disseminated from this location during dental manipulation. The resulting bacteremia may seed abnormal heart valves and produce endocarditis. Unlike pneumococci, they are not soluble in bile.

165. The answer is B. *(Wintrobe, ed 7. p 1801.)* The majority of cases of bacterial meningitis can be attributed to three organisms: *H. influenzae, D. pneumoniae,* and *N. meningitidis*. *S. aureus* meningitis is frequently secondary to trauma or brain abscess. *Salmonella, Clostridium* and *Shigella* are only rarely involved in the pathogenesis of meningitis.

166. The answer is C. *(Burrows, ed 20. p 231. Jawetz, ed 11. p 231.)* Yaws is an endemic tropical infection caused by *Treponema pertenue*. The organism is closely related to the spirochete that causes syphilis and will give a biologic true-positive VDRL. Unlike syphilis, however, yaws is not transmitted venereally but by person-to-person contact.

167. The answer is B. *(Jawetz, ed 11. p 360.)* Yellow fever is an arbovirus infection transmitted by the bite of the Aedes mosquito. It is found in South America and Africa. Dengue fever, also an Aedes-born arbovirus is usually a more benign infection characterized by fever, muscle and joint pain, and lymphadenopathy. Kala-azar is caused by a parasite; scrub typhus by rickettsiae.

168. The answer is B. *(Wintrobe, ed 7. p 775.)* During the clinical course of staphylococcal pneumonia, abscess formation and necrosis develop throughout the lung parenchyma. The abscesses then rupture into bronchial walls or the pleural cavity producing pyopneumothorax or pneumatoceles.

169. The answer is B. *(Burrows, ed 20. p 756. Wintrobe, ed 7. p 880.)* The typical lesion of primary syphilis is the chancre which commonly develops within three weeks of exposure. Chancres may be found on the external genitalia, cervix, anus, or mouth. A diagnosis can be made by darkfield examination or by a positive VDRL test. Tabes dorsalis and gummas are characteristic of late syphilis.

170. The answer is D. *(Davis, ed 2. p 748.)* Cultures for *N. meningitidis* should be taken from the posterior nasopharynx for maximal yield. Staphylococci are usually found in the nasal vestibule and anterior nasopharynx. Pneumococci, α- and β-hemolytic streptococci, and *H. influenzae* should be isolated from the tonsils and lower pharynx.

171. The answer is D. *(Wintrobe, ed 7. p 834.)* Donovan bodies are gram-negative coccobacillary organisms thought to be the cause of granuloma inguinale. They are found in association with the encapsulated bacterium *Calymmatobacterium granulomatis*. Transmitted by sexual intercourse, granuloma inguinale causes a painless nonhealing ulceration of the genitals which may be mistaken for carcinoma.

172. The answer is E. *(Wintrobe, ed 7. pp 839-840.)* Vincent's stomatitis (trench mouth) is an ulcerative condition affecting the oral mucous membranes. Typically, the spirochete *Borrelia vincentii* and the bacillus *Fusobacterium plautivincenti (Bacteroides fusiformis)* act synergistically in the development of the infection. Other bacteria, including cocci and bacillus may also play a role. Actinomycetes are not associated with Vincent's stomatitis but cause an unrelated oral lesion.

173. The answer is D. *(Jawetz, ed 11. p 226.)* *Bordetella pertussis* is the causative agent of whooping cough, a highly contagious disease of childhood. Unlike the other hemophilic species, it does not require X or V factors for growth. Its post-infectious immunity is not permanent, but most recurrences are mild and often subclinical.

174. The answer is D. *(Wintrobe, ed 7. p 774.)* *S. aureus* is implicated in the majority of cases of acute osteomyelitis. *Diplococcus pneumoniae* was a common cause in the preantibiotic era. *M. tuberculosis* and gram-negative organisms are less frequently implicated.

175. The answer is B. *(Davis, ed 2. pp 684-685.)* All toxigenic strains of *C. diphtheriae* are lysogenic for β-phage carrying the *tox* gene. The expression of this gene is controlled by the metabolism of the host bacteria. The greatest amount of toxin is produced by bacteria grown on media containing very low amounts of iron.

176. The answer is E. *(Harvey, ed 18. p 1114.)* *Corynbacterium diphtheriae* is a gram-positive rod with club-shaped ends that causes diphtheria. The disease is serious not only because of the severe pharyngitis it may produce, but also because of the potent toxin released in its course.

177. The answer is A. *(Davis, ed 2. p 778.)* Shigellae are responsible for bacillary dysentery. The organisms are heavily excreted in stools but they are fragile and remain viable for only a short period of time. Ideally, rectal swabs should be taken through a sigmoidoscope under direct vision.

178. The answer is E. *(Wintrobe, ed 7. p 788.)* In the female, asymptomatic gonococcal infection involves most frequently the endocervix, and in decreasing order, the urethra, anal canal, and pharynx. Extension of the disease to the fallopian tubes is usually accompanied by the signs and symptoms of acute salpingitis.

179. **The answer is D.** *(Davis, ed 2. pp 736, 774, 839.)* Staphylococcal food poisoning is characterized by an incubation period of 1 to 8 hours. Symptoms include violent nausea, vomiting (often projectile), and diarrhea. Fever is absent and convalescence is usually rapid. The symptoms are due to preformed enterotoxin and not to infection. Food poisoning due to salmonellae does not appear until 1 to 3 days after ingestion of the organisms and fever is commonly noted. *C. perfringens* produces a gastroenteritis about 12 hours after ingestion of contaminated food.

180. **The answer is A.** *(Wintrobe, ed 7. pp 878-880.)* Secondary syphilis appears six to eight weeks after the chancre of primary syphilis. Symptoms include rash, lymphadenopathy, iritis, arthritis, fever and malaise. Argyll Robertson pupil, a small pupil that does not react to light, is a manifestation of neurosyphilis, a late stage of the disease.

181. **The answer is D.** *(Jawetz, ed 11. pp 224-225.)* *H. influenzae* is a gram-negative bacillus. In young children it can cause pneumonitis, sinusitis, otitis, and meningitis. Occasionally it produces a fulminative laryngotracheitis with such severe swelling of the epiglottis that tracheostomy becomes necessary. Clinical infections after the age of three are less frequent.

182. **The answer is B (1, 3).** *(Jawetz, ed 11. pp 177, 184.)* Pneumonia may be caused by any of the organisms mentioned, as well as by a wide variety of other bacteria, fungi, and viruses. However, diplococci and staphylococci are among the more frequent causative agents.

183. **The answer is E (all).** *(Jawetz, ed 11. pp 210, 230, 245, 438.)* The diseases mentioned are all venereal diseases. Lymphogranuloma venerum is caused by a *Chlamydia*; herpes by a virus; condyloma latum by a spirochete; and granuloma inguinale by a gram-negative bacterium.

184. **The answer is B (1, 3).** *(Jawetz, ed 11. p 205.)* *Mycobacteria leprae* are acid-fast bacilli. Although they were the first bacteria to be associated with human disease, they have never been grown on artificial media. There are no diagnostic serologic tests for *M. leprae* although it can cause false-positive VDRL's.

185. **The answer is E (all).** *(Jawetz, ed 11. pp 229-235.)* The causative organisms of yaws (*Treponema pertenue*), pinta (*T. carateum*), syphilis (*T. pallidum*), and relapsing fever (*Borrelia recurrentis*) are all spirochetes, members of the order Spirochaetales. Other diseases caused by spirochetes include Weil's disease (*Leptospira icterohemorrhagiae*), and rat-bite fever (*Spirillum minus*).

186. The answer is E (all). *(Burrows, ed 20. p 422.)* Streptococci produce a variety of toxic products including streptolysin (a hemolysin), streptokinase (a fibrinolysin), erythrogenic toxin (scarlatinal toxin) and hyaluronidase (spreading factor). These organisms also produce leukocidin and enterotoxin.

187. The answer is E (all). *(Merritt, ed 5. p 123.)* Tabes dorsalis is said to have a triad of symptoms (pain, dysuria, ataxia) and a triad of signs (Argyll Robertson pupils, absent reflexes, and loss of proprioception), It is an infrequent manifestation of tertiary syphilis.

188. The answer is B (1, 3). *(Davis, ed 2. p 759.)* Deoxycholate agar is used for the isolation of enteric bacilli from stool specimens. The medium contains bile salts that inhibit the growth of the gram-positive cocci normally found in feces. The incorporation of neutral red allows lactose fermenters to be differentiated by the pink color which develops in the colonies. Glucose is not present in the agar.

189. The answer is C (2, 4). *(Jawetz, ed 11. p 177.)* While no absolute criteria exist, *S. aureus* is considered to be pathogenic if it produces coagulase or hemolyzes blood. Other criteria, of less reliability, include the production of yellow pigment, fermentation of mannitol, and liquefaction of gelatin.

190. The answer is E (all). *(Davis, ed 2. pp 749-751.)* *N. gonorrhoeae* is a nonmotile, nonspore-forming gram-negative diplococci. It is a difficult organism to culture, but grows luxuriantly on chocolate agar (heated blood agar) or Thayer-Martin medium (a selective chocolate agar). The organism is fastidious in its requirement for a 3-10% CO_2 atmosphere. Penicillin is the treatment of choice for *N. gonorrhoeae* infections.

191. The answer is B (1, 3). *(Davis, ed 2. pp 865-867.)* *Mycobacterium leprae*, the causative organism of human leprosy, is virtually indistinguishable in morphology and staining properties from *M. tuberculosis*. Although *M. leprae* grows profusely in lesions, it has never been cultivated in vitro. Drug therapy with diaminodiphenylsulfone for prolonged periods of time is the preferred therapy. The mode of transmission of this disease is uncertain, however, it is believed to be man-to-man.

192. The answer is A (1, 2, 3). *(Jawetz, ed 11. p 24.)* Among the clinically important bacteria all the cocci are gram-positive except *Neisseria*. All the bacilli are gram-negative except *Clostridium, Corynebacterium, Listeria,* and *Erysipelothrix. Pseudomonas* is an enteric gram-negative rod.

193. The answer is E (all). *(Burrows, ed 20. pp 664, 727, 880, 882.)* Granulomatous lesions are well circumscribed nodular reactions to irritating stimuli. They are characterized by the presence of macrophages and may persist for prolonged periods of time as sites of smoldering inflammation. Granulomas are found in a variety of diseases caused by microorganisms (including all those mentioned above) and by chemical and mineral matter.

194. The answer is C (2, 4). *(Jawetz, ed 11. pp 214, 217.)* Salmonella-Shigella (SS) agar is a medium that is useful for the isolation of these organisms from heavily contaminated specimens, i.e., feces. It contains bile salts to inhibit the growth of most gram-positive organisms and citrate to inhibit the growth of coliforms. Wilson-Blair bismuth sulfite agar is another medium useful for the isolation of salmonellae. Cultures of salmonellae grown on this medium are characterisitically black in color.

195. The answer is C (2, 4). *(Jawetz, ed 11. pp 186-187.)* The neisseriae are strict aerobes; they require the presence of atmospheric oxygen. They grow poorly on media containing salts or fatty acids, while their growth is enhanced by high CO_2 tension. For these reasons, when cultures are taken for neisseriae, they should be placed in a candle jar and incubated immediately.

196. The answer is E (all). *(Jawetz, ed 11. pp 169-170.)* Erysipelas and impetigo are streptococcal skin infections which commonly occur in children. In a very small percentage of cases (0.5 percent) these infections initiate acute glomerulonephritis. Puerperal fever is an infection of the uterus which occurs when streptococci enter the uterus after delivery.

197. The answer is E (all). *(Jawetz, ed 11. p 193.)* Tetanus may be treated with penicillin, tetanus antitoxin, tetanus toxoid, or debridement of wounds. These measures are attempts to decrease the formation and deposition of toxin. They have no effect on toxin that is already bound to nerve tissue and which may persist symptomatically for weeks.

198. The answer is E (all). *(Jawetz, ed 11. p 255.)* The predominant microorganisms of the skin include diphtheroid bacilli, nonhemolytic staphylococci, *Streptococcus viridans*, *S. faecalis*, mimeae, fungi, and yeasts. Neither washing nor surgical scrubbing can make the skin completely sterile.

199. The answer is C (2, 4). *(Davis, ed 2. p 867.)* Leprosy is a chronic infection that produces large firm cutaneous nodules and destruction of peripheral nerves. While endemic to parts of South American and Asia, it is not uncommon in the U.S.A.; especially in Texas and Louisiana. The disease is not usually fatal in itself, but it is frequently complicated by concurrent illness such as tuberculosis or amyloidosis. Leprosy frequently produces a false-positive Wassermann test.

200. The answer is A (1, 2, 3). *(Davis, ed 2. pp 807-809.)* *Pasteurella tularensis* is a short, non-motile, gram-negative organism that is markedly pleomorphic. It has a rigid growth requirement for cysteine. Human tularemia is usually acquired from direct contact with tissues of infected rabbits, but is also transmitted by the bites of flies and ticks. It causes a variety of clinical syndromes including ulceroglandular, oculoglandular, pneumonic, and typhoidal tularemia.

201. The answer is E (all). *(Burrows, ed 20. p 650.)* Diphtheria is caused by a toxin producing strain of corynebacteria (*C. diphtheriae*). Immunity to this toxin (and therefore to the disease) may be demonstrated by the Schick test. However, healthy individuals, even without immunity, may harbor the bacteria in their pharynx without apparent disease. Löffler's medium is an enriched medium that supports the growth of these organisms.

202. The answer is E (all). *(Burrows, ed 20. p 496.)* *Salmonella* gastroenteritis is characterized by a short incubation period which ranges from 8 to 48 hours, acute vomiting, and diarrhea. Patients usually have rapid recovery. The disease is most often acquired by ingestion of contaminated food.

203. The answer is C (2, 4). *(Jawetz, ed 11. pp 190-191.)* *Bacillus anthracis* is a gram-positive rod. Its capsular substance is not a polysaccharide but a polypeptide of high molecular weight. In animals, this bacteria is responsible for severe septicemia (anthrax). In man, it causes woolsorter's disease (a primary pneumonia) and malignant pustules.

204. The answer is A (1, 2). *(Jawetz, ed 11. pp 176, 193, 197.)* The elaboration of potent protein exotoxin is responsible for the clinical manifestations of diphtheria, tetanus, and many staphylococcal infections. Some clostridia, streptococci, pasteurellae, bordetellae, and shigellae also produce exotoxin. *M. tuberculosis* is an invasive organism, whose pathogenicity is related to bacterial multiplication.

205. The answer is D (4). *(Jawetz, ed 11. p 231.)* Bejel is a highly infectious skin disease which occurs primarily in Africa and is commonly seen in children. The disease is caused by a spirochete, indistinguishable from *Treponema pallidum*, the causative organism of syphilis. Bejel is, however, a nonvenereal disease transmitted by direct contact.

206. The answer is A (1, 2, 3). *(Jawetz, ed 11. p 193.)* Flagella are responsible for the motility of most eubacteria. Most clostridia possess flagella and are therefore motile. Streptococci, staphylococci, and neisseriae lack this structure and are nonmotile.

207. The answer is D (4). *(Davis, ed 2. p 750.)* The portal of entry of gonococci is usually the mucous membrane of the urethra, cervix, rectum, or pharynx. They cannot penetrate intact squamous epithelium easily. A biochemical test that distinguishes between gonococci and meningococci is the latter's ability to ferment maltose. Ophthalmia neonatorum is an eye infection of the newborn caused by gonococci.

208. The answer is E (all). *(Davis, ed 2. pp 745-749.)* Meningococcal infection usually begins as pharyngitis and then may spread to the meninges, lungs, or joints. Meningococci produce an endotoxin which can cause extensive vascular damage. Acute adrenal insufficiency (Waterhouse-Friderichsen syndrome) may result. The virulence of meningococci depends on the presence of capsules.

209. The answer is E (all). *(Jawetz, ed 11. pp 207-208.)* Endotoxins of gram-negative bacteria are heat-stable lipopolysaccharides derived from the cell wall. They are responsible for many of the symptoms and complications of gram-negative infections including fever, DIC, leukopenia, and hemorrhagic necrosis. The Shwartzman phenomenon is a complex reaction to experimentally injected endotoxin.

210. The answer is D (4). *(Jawetz, ed 11. pp 184, 228.)* Chancroid is a venereal disease caused by *Hemophilus ducreyi* a small gram-negative rod. Meningococci and gonococci are gram-negative cocci. Ludwig's angina is an infection of the oral cavity, in the region of the submaxillary gland, usually caused by streptococci.

211. The answer is A (1, 2, 3). *(Jawetz, ed 11. pp 232-233.)* Relapsing fever is characterized by the sudden onset of chills, fever, and headache. There is often splenomegly and jaundice. The fever ends abruptly in 3 to 4 days, but usually recurs 2 to 14 days later. Relapses are thought to be due to alterations in the antigenic structure of *Borrelia recurrentis*, the causative organism. Diarrhea is not a common symptom.

212. The answer is C (2, 4). *(Jawetz, ed 11. pp 231-232.)* Yaws is an infection caused by *Treponema pertenue.* Characteristically there are ulcers on the arms and legs. The disease remains localized and dissemination is rare. The usual complications are scarring and local bone destruction.

213. The answer is A (1, 2, 3). *(Davis, ed 2. pp 704-705.)* Pneumococci and viridans streptococci are often confused on Gram stain. Pneumococci are generally bile-soluble, sensitive to optochin, and virulent for mice. Both streptococci and pneumococci are catalase-negative and can produce α-hemolysis on blood agar.

214. The answer is D (4). *(Davis, ed 2. p 683.)* The capsules of *D. pneumoniae*, *B. anthracis*, and *K. pneumoniae* are antiphagocytic and play a role in the pathogenicity of these organisms. *C. diphtheriae* is nonencapsulated. Its pathogenicity is dependent on exotoxin.

215. The answer is E (all). *(Jawetz, ed 11. p 253.)* Bacteroides are part of the normal flora of the respiratory and intestinal tracts. They are anaerobic bacteria that have been recently implicated with increasing frequency in a large number of clinical infections of the lung and brain, and in postoperative abdominal abscesses. Laboratory diagnosis rests on strict anaerobic culture techniques. Most bacteroides (except *B. fragilis*) are sensitive to penicillin.

216. The answer is B (1, 3). *(Jawetz, ed 11. p 175.)* The spectrum of staphylococcal disease ranges from minor skin infections (carbuncles and impetigo) to life-threatening meningitis and pneumonia. Pertussis or "whooping cough" is caused by *Bordetella pertussis*. Scarlet fever is a manifestation of β-streptococcal infection.

217. The answer is E (all). *(Jawetz, ed 11. p 224.)* Vaccines against *Pasteurella pestis* may be prepared from avirulent live bacteria, heat-killed or formalin-inactivated virulent bacteria, and chemical fractions of the bacilli. These vaccines provide some immunity to bubonic plague, but not to pneumonic plague. Prophylactic tetracycline provides efficient protection.

218-222. The answers are: 218-C, 219-D, 220-B, 221-A, 222-E. *(Jawetz, ed 11. pp 130-133.)* All five drugs listed are or have been commonly used in treating tuberculosis. Cycloserine (D-4-amino-3-isoxazolidinone) acts by inhibiting the incorporation of D-alanine into bacterial cell walls. Occasionally, it is administered for urinary tract infections. It can cause neurotoxic side-effects or shock. While infrequent, hypersensitivity to ethambutol most commonly manifests itself in visual disturbances. Patients taking INH excrete pyridoxine in excess amounts which leads to peripheral neuritis. The administration of pyridoxine (0.3 - 0.5 gm daily) prevents this and does not counteract the antituberculous effect of INH. Full oral doses of PAS for treatment of tuberculosis have been commonly associated with severe gastrointestinal distress, and PAS is used now only rarely. Streptomycin is extremely toxic for the vestibular portion of the eighth cranial nerve, causing ataxia, vertigo, and tinnitus.

223-227. The answers are: 223-D, 224-D, 225-B, 226-A, 227-C. *(Jawetz, ed. 11. pp 288-289.)* Preferred culture media for *Bacteroides* and *Clostridium* include chopped meat broth, thioglycollate medium, and blood agar plates. Corynebacteria grow on most ordinary laboratory media but grow more readily on Löffler's serum than do other respiratory pathogenic bacteria. *N. meningitidis* and *N. gonorrhoeae* grow best on media containing complex organic substances such as blood or animal proteins and, in contrast to other neisseriae, will not grow on plain nutrient agar. Mycobacteria grow more slowly than do most bacteria and can be encouraged to grow in some media by the addition of Tween 80.

Physiology

228. The answer is D. *(Jawetz, ed 11. pp 122-123.)* The structural integrity of the beta-lactam ring in penicillins is essential for antimicrobial activity. Many resistant strains of staphylococci produce an enzyme, penicillinase, that cleaves the β-lactam ring at the position numbered 4 on the diagram shown. Other organisms, including certain coliform bacteria, produce an amidase enzyme that inactivates penicillin by action at position 1.

229. The answer is C. *(Jawetz, ed 11. pp 184-185.)* If pneumococci are mixed with specific antisera the capsules swell markedly. When employed diagnostically, this reaction is referred to as the quellung test. It is a useful means of rapidly identifying pneumococci in sputum smears.

230. The answer is D. *(Jawetz, ed 11. p 89.)* Antimicrobial agents interfere with cellular integrity and growth through a variety of pathways. These include protein coagulation (heat), cell wall disruption (penicillin), removal of free sulfhydryl groups (heavy metals), poisoning of respiratory enzymes (carbon monoxide and cyanide), and antagonism of oxidative phosphorylation (dinitrophenol). Dinitrophenol inhibits the energy-yielding process necessary for cell growth and reproduction.

231. The answer is D. *(Jawetz, ed 11. pp 87-88.)* Antimicrobial agents that inhibit bacterial multiplication but allow multiplication to resume upon their removal are bacteriostatic. Bactericidal agents kill bacteria. Bactericidal action differs from bacteriostasis only in being irreversible.

232. The answer is C. *(Jawetz, ed 11. pp 11-12.)* Mucopeptides (also called peptidoglycans or murein) are major components of both gram-positive and gram-negative cell walls. They provide the tensile strength that allows bacteria to maintain an internal osmotic pressure of 5-20 atmospheres. Lysozymes act by attacking the mucopeptides, causing weakening of the wall and cell lysis.

233. The answer is D. *(Davis, ed 2. p 130.)* When a bacterial cell, especially a gram-negative cell, is exposed to a hypertonic solution, the membrane and its contents contract and shrink away from the wall. This is called plasmolysis and demonstrates the presence of a rigid cell wall outside the cytoplasmic membrane.

234. The answer is B. *(Jawetz, ed 11. pp 196-197.)* All toxigenic strains of *Corynebacterium diphtheriae* can elaborate a potent necrotizing exotoxin. Diphtheria toxin is a heat-labile polypeptide of which a 40 ng dose is lethal for animals. The toxin inhibits polypeptide chain elongation through inactivation of the elongation factor (EF-2). This results in necrosis of heart, muscle, liver, kidneys, and adrenals.

235. The answer is A. *(Burrows, ed 20. pp 19-20.)* Flagella (as pictured) are organelles of motility. They are long filamentous structures originating in a spherical structure, the basal body. The internal structure is characteristic: nine peripheral fibrils surround two central fibrils. F pili, organs of conjugation, are shorter and straighter than flagella.

236. The answer is B. *(Davis, ed 2. p 772.)* The tendency of *Proteus* organisms to swarm, i.e., to form a thin spreading growth, is the result of their active motility, and makes isolation of these organisms difficult. Five % agar, or the addition of chloral hydrate to 1 to 2% agar, inhibits swarming. *Proteus* is a lactose-negative bacterium.

237. The answer is B. *(Davis, ed 2. pp 36-37.)* In vertebrates, the GC base content of DNA remains constant at approximately 40 mole %. In bacteria, the content varies between 30 and 70 mole %. The GC/AT ratio is the same for a strain of bacterium throughout all segments of its chromosome. It represents a constant characteristic suitable for taxonomic maps of bacterial evolution.

238. The answer is B. *(Burrows, ed 20. pp 162-163.)* Penicillin acts on actively growing cells. It inhibits the synthesis of bacterial cell walls by blocking the terminal cross-linkage of glycopeptides. Vancomycin and bacitracin also exert their antimicrobial action through impairment of cell wall synthesis.

239. The answer is D. *(Burrows, ed 20. p 235.)* Endotoxins are structural components of the lipopolysaccharide cell wall complex of gram-negative bacteria. They are heat-stable, but susceptible to mild acid hydrolysis. They may be responsible, in part, for many of the effects of severe gram-negative infection, including fever, leukopenia, thrombocytopenia, and shock.

240. The answer is B. *(Davis, ed 2. p 28.)* Bacterial flagella are composed of flagellin, a protein that can have a molecular weight of 50,000. This protein sometimes contains a novel amino acid, ∈ N-methyl-lysine.

241. The answer is A. *(Davis, ed 2. pp 22-23.)* Gram's staining method involves the application of a basic dye, crystal violet, followed by iodine for fixation. The preparation is then treated with ethanol which decolorizes gram-negative bacteria. Finally, a counterstain, safranin, is applied to restain the decolorized organisms.

242. The answer is C. *(Davis, ed 2. p 716.)* The M protein of streptococci is a surface antigen which is useful in the typing of these organisms. It gives antiphagocytic properties to the organism and is directly involved in virulence. In *E. coli* there is an unrelated M protein which functions in the transport of lactose.

243. The answer is B. *(Jones, J Biol Chem 244:5981-5987.)* Lactose permease is a membrane-associated enzyme which helps to facilitate the transport of β-galactosides. Its molecular weight is about 30,000.

244. The answer is C. *(Davis, ed 2. pp 714-716.)* The β-hemolytic streptococci are separated into groups A to O on the basis of the C carbohydrate antigens in their cell walls. They are further broken down into more than 55 immunologic types by their M proteins.

245. The answer is E. *(Davis, ed 2. pp 697-698, 770.)* The invasive properties of *K. pneumoniae*, like those of *D. pneumoniae*, are dependent upon the antiphagocytic properties of the capsules: unencapsulated strains are avirulent. Both these organisms may cause pneumonia. *Klebsiella* is a frequent offender in patients with underlying chronic lung disease.

246. The answer is A. *(Davis, ed 2. pp 25, 943-944.)* Protoplasts are gram-positive bacteria and spheroplasts are gram-negative bacteria that have had their rigid cell walls digested by lysozymes. They must be maintained in a hypertonic medium to prevent lysis. L forms are bacteria with defective or absent walls that arise spontaneously under favorable conditions such as high salt concentrations or when wall synthesis is impaired by penicillin. Their role in human disease is unclear.

247. The answer is D. *(Davis, ed 2. pp 177-178.)* The auxotroph revertant must be allowed to grow so that nuclear divisions to segregate a mutant recessive allele and for cytoplasmic expression of the new gene product can occur. During this brief period of time, the "phenotypic lag," the required nutrient must be supplied.

248. The answer is A. *(Davis, ed 2. p 143.)* While many spores germinate spontaneously, others will not germinate unless they are exposed to a traumatic stimulus. This process is referred to as activation. Simple aging is probably the most frequent activating stimulus.

249. The answer is E. *(Jawetz, ed 11. pp 45-47.)* Transfer factor is functional in delayed hypersensitivity reactions. Plasmids are small, bacterial, extrachromosomal genetic elements, unrelated to eukaryotic transfer factor. Plasmids include the sex (F) factors, col factors (colicin producing), R factors (antibiotic resistance), and the penicillinase plasmids. Transfer factor is a noncellular extract of T lymphocytes which imparts cell-mediated hypersensitivity.

250. The answer is A. *(Davis, ed 2. p 108.)* The fracture shows concave and convex plasma membrane surfaces.

251. The answer is A (1, 2, 3). *(Davis, ed 2. p 22.)* Because of their thicker cell walls gram-positive organisms are usually more resistant to drying than gram-negative organisms. Endotoxins are produced only by gram-negative bacteria. Both gram-positive and gram-negative bacteria may possess capsules.

252. The answer is D (4). *(Davis, ed 2. pp 108, 122.)* Freeze-etching is a method of preparing cells for electron microscopy. During the procedure the cell membrane bilayer is split revealing freeze-etch particles. The particles are thought to represent globular proteins within the hydrophobic region of the membrane. Freeze-etching eliminates many of the alterations induced by other methods of fixation.

253. The answer is C (2, 4). *(Copenhaver, ed 16. p 44.)* On the exterior surface of virtually all animal cells, there is a layer of carbohydrates and associated lipids and proteins, known as the glycocalyx. This layer contributes to the surface properties of the cell.

254. The answer is A (1, 2, 3). *(Davis, ed 2. pp 123, 134.)* The periplasm is the substance which lies in the periplasmic space, i.e., the space between the plasma membrane and the cell wall. In addition to various enzymes, it contains binding proteins, which are involved in membrane transport of certain amino acids and sugars. Only gram-negative organisms possess these features: gram-positive bacteria lack both binding proteins and a well defined periplasmic space.

255. The answer is C (2, 4). *(Davis, ed 2. p 44.)* *Propionibacterium, C. acnes,* and *A. propionica* are capable of fermenting pyruvate to yield propionic acid and CO_2, and generating ATP in the process. The pathway so extracts further energy from the substrate. This reaction is important in the commercial manufacturing of swiss cheese where carbon dioxide is responsible for the holes and propionic acid is responsible for the odor and flavor.

256. The answer is E (all). *(Davis, ed 2. pp 137-139, 141.)* All spores, including those of *B. subtilis,* exhibit all the characteristics listed. Three groups of gram-positive organisms possess the ability to form spores: clostridia, bacilli, and sporosarcinae. The function of the calcium in spores may be to contract the loose polyanionic cortical peptidoglycan, expelling water and contributing to structual strength. Sporulation is initiated when culture conditions become unfavorable. Depletion of nitrogen and carbon is thought to play a key role.

257. The answer is C (2, 4). *(Davis, ed 2. p 108.)* The organisms illustrated are spheroplasts of *E. coli*. Spheroplasts are bacteria which have had their cell walls partially removed by the action of lysozyme or penicillin. Ordinarily, with disintegration of the walls, the cells undergo lysis. However, in a hypertonic medium, the cells persist and assume a spherical configuration.

258. The answer is A (1, 2, 3). *(Lehninger, 1970. p 235.)* A peptidoglycan framework is the basis of both gram-positive and gram-negative cell walls. This complex network imparts rigidity to the cell and is the substrate for lysozyme action. In addition, the cell walls of gram-negative organisms are rich in lipopolysaccharides and other complex lipids. Gram-positive cell walls are lipid-poor.

259. The answer is E (all). *(Jawetz, ed 11. pp 83-84.)* Microbial growth is closely dependent upon temperature, time, the size of the initial inoculum, and the constituents of the medium. Other factors include pH, osmotic pressure, salt concentration, and aeration.

260. The answer is C (2, 4). *(Davis, ed 2. p 844.)* The common acid-fast bacilli include the mycobacteria, causative agents of leprosy and tuberculosis. Their name comes from their ability to resist decolorization by acidified solvents after staining.

261. The answer is E (all). *(Jawetz, ed 11. p 119.)* All of the negative effects listed may be seen with indiscriminate use of antibiotics. The rational use of antimicrobial drugs demands that a specific etiologic diagnosis be made before antibiotics are administered, and that due consideration be given to each drug's adverse effects.

262. The answer is B (1, 3). *(Davis, ed 2. p 108.)* Freeze-etch particles in *E. coli* appear in the cell membrane, on the face marked A in the photograph.

263. The answer is A (1, 2, 3). *(Burrows, ed 20. p 25.)* The term acid-fast refers to the ability of certain bacteria to resist decolorization, even with acid-alcohol. This property is due in part to the high lipid content. Mycobacteria, as well as certain actinomycetes, are acid-fast.

264. The answer is C (2, 4). *(Jawetz, ed 11. p 137.)* Endotoxins are lipopolysaccharide components of the cell walls of certain gram-negative rods that are released upon the rods' disintegration. Unlike exotoxins, they are heat-stable, often pyrogenic, are not converted into toxoids, and often cause fever.

265. The answer is B (1, 3). *(Jawetz, ed 11. p 84.)* In bacterial cultures, the lag phase is a period of synthesis in which the cells prepare for growth by forming new enzymes and intermediates, or by mutation. Growth is maximal during the exponential phase, and again reaches a steady state during the maximum stationary phase. Cell death is prominent during the decline phase.

266. The answer is A (1, 2, 3). *(Jawetz, ed 11. p 139.)* When a phagocytic cell "eats" a microorganism, oxygen consumption, glycolysis, and RNA turnover increase. The phagocytes undergo degranulation and release enzymes from their lysosomes.

267. The answer is D (4). *(Davis, ed 2. p 177.)* A methionine auxotrophic mutant cannot synthesize methionine and is unable, therefore, to grow in a methionine-free medium. Penicillin attacks only actively multiplying cells and cannot, therefore, affect auxotrophs when they are growing in deficient media. Auxotrophs must be grown in media enriched with the essential components that they are unable to produce. The growth of mutants may be temperature sensitive in enriched medium, but this characteristic is not true of all methionine-requiring auxotrophs.

268. The answer is D (4). *(Davis, ed 2. p 72.)* Dipicolinic acid, formed in the synthesis of DAP, is a prominent component of spores but is not found in vegetative cells. It apparently plays an important role in stabilizing cellular proteins but its mechanism of action is unknown.

269. The answer is A (1, 2, 3). *(Davis, ed 2. p 1462.)* Ethanol acts as a disinfectant through protein denaturation, a property enhanced by the presence of water. Ethanol is most effective in concentrations of 50-70%. At concentrations of 100%, or less than 20%, its bactericidal action is poor.

270. The answer is E (all). *(Jawetz, ed 11. p 137.)* All the statements listed about exotoxins are correct. Exotoxins are produced by a variety of bacteria including *Clostridium tetani, Clostridium botulinum,* and *Corynebacterium diphtheriae.*

271. The answer is C (2, 4). *(Davis, ed 2. p 195.)* The F pilus is a conjugative apparatus possessed only by "male" bacteria. It is a tubular structure that serves to transfer genetic information between organisms.

272. The answer is C (2, 4). *(Davis, ed 2. p 110.)* Peptidoglycans are components of the cell walls of all bacteria except mycoplasmas and certain halophilic bacteria. They are composed of backbones of N-acetylmuramate and N-acetylglucosamine to which cross-linked peptides are attached.

273. The answer is E (all). *(Davis, ed 2. p 1454.)* Pasteurization was used initially to control the bitterness of wine, and is now used primarily in milk processing. It consists of heating a substance at 62° C for 30 minutes, or at higher temperatures for a fraction of a minute. Total bacterial counts are thereby reduced by 97 to 99 percent.

274. The answer is A (1, 2, 3). *(Davis, ed 2. p 1455.)* Most bacteria, fungi, and viruses are sterilized by boiling for 10 to 15 minutes. However, spores may not be killed by this method. For absolute sterility, autoclaving for 15 minutes at 121° C is recommended. Because proteins are more easily denatured in the presence of water, moist heat is preferable to dry heat.

275-280. The answers are: 275-D, 276-A, 277-E, 278-B, 279-C, 280-C. *(Ames, J Biol Chem 249:634.)* Gel electrophoresis provides a rapid method for identifying bacterial proteins and estimating molecular weights. Band E represents the dye front. The other bands identify the following proteins: D—lactose permease (mol wt 30,000); A—RNA polymerases (mol wt 155,000); and C—flagellin and the major cell wall protein (mol wt 50,000).

281-285. The answers are: 281-D, 282-A, 283-C, 284-B, 285-E. *(Davis, ed 2. p 24.)* Each bacteria listed is matched with its characteristic form. Other bacterial forms include sarcinae (cocci in square tetrads or cubical packets of eight cells), coccobacilli (short rods), fusiform bacilli (oval tapered rods), and filamentous forms (long, thready rods).

286-289. The answers are: 286-C, 287-D, 288-B, 289-A. *(Davis, ed 2. pp 150-152, 160.)* Penicillin lyses and kills the growing cells; it is immediately bactericidal. Chloramphenicol causes an immediate, reversible, bacteriostatic inhibition of protein synthesis. Sulfonamide competes for para-aminobenzoic acid and causes a gradual depletion of intracellular folate as the cells continue to grow. Like chloramphenicol, it is a bacteriostatic agent.

290-294. The answers are: 290-C, 291-C, 292-B, 293-A, 294-E. *(Jawetz, ed 11. pp 121-135.)* The aminoglycosides (streptomycin, etc.), as well as chloramphenicol, bind to ribosomes and block protein synthesis. Penicillin exerts its antimicrobial effect by impairment of cell wall synthesis. Polymyxin has a direct action on cell membrane function. The sulfonamides mimic para-aminobenzoic acid in the synthesis of folic acid, thus competing for this essential metabolite.

295-298. The answers are: 295-A, 296-C, 297-D, 298-B. *(Van Gool, J Bacteriol 108:474-481, 1971.)* Concave fractures, from the inside of the envelope out, are: plasma membrane; peptidoglycan layer; and cell wall lipopolysaccharide layer.

Rickettsiae, Chlamydiae, and Mycoplasmas

299. The answer is D. *(Davis, ed 2. p 901.)* The rickettsiae were once believed to occupy a special taxonomic class between bacteria and viruses. However, they are now considered to be bacteria because of the following characteristics: 1) They contain both RNA and DNA; 2) They are responsive to antibiotics; 3) They reproduce by binary fission; 4) They share many metabolic and chemical characteristics of bacteria.

300. The answer is C. *(Burrows, ed 20. p 838.)* Tsutsugamushi fever (scrub typhus) is prevalent in the Far East. It is transmitted by a trombiculial mite and is often characterized by the formation of an eschar at the mite bite site. Rash and fever are prominent signs, with the fever usually subsiding in approximately three weeks, but total recovery sometimes requiring months.

301. The answer is E. *(Davis, ed 2. p 926.)* Ornithosis (psittacosis) is caused by *Chlamydia psittaci*, and is usually contracted from infected birds kept either as pets, on poultry farms, or in poultry dressing plants. Although ornithosis may be asymptomatic in man, severe and fatal pneumonia can develop. Fortunately, it is easily cured with tetracycline.

302. The answer is D. *(Jawetz, ed 11. p 237.)* Because of antigenic similarities between rickettsiae and *Proteus* organisms, the sera of individuals with endemic typhus will agglutinate certain strains of *Proteus vulgaris*. This reaction, known as the Weil-Felix reaction, is used clinically in the diagnosis of rickettsial infections. Other serologic tests, as well as intraperitoneal injections in laboratory animals, may also be used to identify rickettsial disease.

303. The answer is D. *(Davis, ed 2. pp 911-912.)* Most rickettsial diseases are transmitted to humans via arthropod vectors. The only exception is *Coxiella burneti*, the causative agent of Q fever, which is transmitted by inhalation of contaminated dust and aerosols.

304. The answer is E. *(Davis, ed 2. p 906.)* Antibodies formed during the course of many rickettsial diseases cross-react to the antigens of certain *Proteus* organisms. This is true for epidemic and endemic typhus, Rocky Mountain spotted fever, and scrub typhus. *Proteus* antigens are usually negative in rickettsialpox, Q fever, trench fever and Brill's disease.

305. The answer is C. *(Davis, ed 2. p 936.)* The role of mycoplasmas in human disease was unknown until the demonstration of *Mycoplasma pneumoniae* as a causative agent of primary atypical pneumonia. Mycoplasmas are also suspected to be the causative agents in nongonococcal urethritis.

306. The answer is D. *(Jawetz, ed 11. p 238.)* Rickettsial growth is enhanced by sulfonamide, and consequently it is contraindicated in rickettsial diseases. Para-aminobenzoic acid, a structural analog of sulfonamide, inhibits the growth of these organisms. Rickettsial infections may be satisfactorily treated with chloramphenicol or tetracycline.

307. The answer is D. *(Jawetz, ed 11. p 241.)* Unlike the other organisms listed, mycoplasmas lack cell walls. Because of this fact, they are highly pleomorphic and completely resistant to the action of penicillin. Despite the superficial resemblance, these organisms are not genetically related to the wall-defective microbial forms (i.e., spheroplasts and protoplasts).

308. The answer is A. *(Jawetz, ed 11. pp 236-237.)* *Rickettsia rickettsi*, the etiologic agent of Rocky Mountain spotted fever, is found in the saliva of the wood tick *Dermacentor andersoni* and the dog tick *D. variabilis*. The organisms can be transmitted to man via the tick's bite. The disease is not limited to the Rocky Mountains.

309. The answer is D. *(Burrows, ed 20. pp 497, 837.)* Typhoid fever is caused by *Salmonella typhosa*. It is a bacterial disease which causes fever, abdominal pain, and, in severe cases, intestinal hemmorhage. The term typhus refers to a group of rickettsial diseases including epidemic and endemic typhus. These diseases are characterized by rash, fever, and hepatosplenomegaly.

310. The answer is A. *(Davis, ed 2. pp 921-922.)* Chlamydiae share with bacteria many metabolic pathways that are sensitive to the actions of antibiotics. Group A organisms, the agents of trachoma, lymphogranuloma venereum, and inclusion conjunctivitis, usually respond to sulfonamides. Group B organisms, such as the agents or ornithosis, are treated with tetracyclines.

311. The answer is C (2, 4). *(Davis, ed 2. pp 916-918.)* While both chlamydiae and viruses are obligate intracellular parasites, and depend on the host cell for metabolic energy, they differ in many respects. Unlike viruses, chlamydiae synthesize proteins, are sensitive to antibiotics, and reproduce by fission. Chlamydiae are readily seen under the light microscope and possess bacterial-type cell walls.

312. The answer is E (all). *(Jawetz, ed 11. p 245.)* Lymphogranuloma venerum is a venereal disease caused by chlamydiae. It has three stages: a papule stage, an inguinal bubo stage, and a fibrosis stage. In women, because of the lymphatic drainage to the perirectal nodes, obstruction and fistulas may appear as late sequelae of the disease. It is uncommon in the U.S.A., but may be found in veterans returning from Vietnam.

313. The answer is E (all). *(Jawetz, ed 11. p 249.)* Mycoplasmas are extremely small, highly pleomorphic organisms which lack cell walls. They can reproduce on artificial media forming small colonies with a "fried egg" appearance. They stain poorly with Gram stain, but well with Giemsa stain. They are resistant to penicillin but sensitive to tetracycline and sulfonamide.

314. The answer is E (all). *(Jawetz, ed 11. pp 250-251.)* Primary atypical pneumonia (PAP) is a disease of multiple etiology. It can be caused by chlamydiae, rickettsiae, fungi, or viral agents. The single most important cause is *Mycoplasma pneumoniae* (Eaton agents). PAP is characterized by fever, cough, and pulmonary infiltrates. Characteristically, when the disease is caused by mycoplasmae, cold-agglutinins appear in the sera.

315. The answer is A (1, 2, 3). *(Jawetz, ed 11. pp 246-247.)* Trachoma, a disease limited to man, is caused by chlamydiae. Worldwide, it probably is the most common cause of blindness, affecting about 400 million people. It is a chronic keratoconjunctivitis which can be treated successfully with sulfonamide and tetracycline. Relapse is, however, common.

316. The answer is A (1, 2, 3). *(Jawetz, ed 11. p 236.)* Rickettsiae are small, nonmotile bacteria which may either appear as short rods or cocci, and whose cell walls resemble those of gram-negative bacteria. Most are obligate intracellular parasites and cannot be grown in cell-free media. *Rochalimaea quintana*, the agent of trench fever, is an exception: it can be cultivated on blood agar. Rat-bite fever is caused by a spirochete.

317. The answer is C (2, 4). *(Jawetz, ed 11. p 237.)* The OX19 Weil-Felix reaction is characteristically strong in epidemic or endemic typhus; weak in Rocky Mountain spotted fever, and absent in rickettsialpox and Q fever. Rocky Mountain spotted fever also agglutinates OX2, but typhus does not. Other more specific serologic reactions, including complement fixation, and antibody and agglutination tests, are also available to distinguish these diseases.

318. The answer is A (1, 2, 3). *(Davis, ed 2. p 911.)* The etiologic agent of Q fever, *Coxiella burneti*, is atypical of rickettsiae. It is stable outside the host cell and is resistant to drying. Transmission to man is by inhalation and not by rodents or arthropod vectors. Rash is not a prominent sign and Weil-Felix antibodies are not found in the sera.

319. The answer is E (all). *(Jawetz, ed 11. pp 236-240.)* All the diseases listed are caused by species of rickettsiae. The agent of trench fever is *Rickettsia quintana* and that of Q fever is *Coxiella burneti*. Both epidemic typhus and Brill's disease are caused by *Rickettsia prowazeki*. Brill's disease is a recrudescence of a previous typhus infection in which latent organisms are reactivated years after the initial exposure.

Mycology

320. The answer is B. *(Jawetz, ed 11. p 266.)* Disseminated candidiasis can be a life-threatening infection when seen in the immunosuppressed patient, or as a secondary invader of the lung, kidney, and other organs in people with tuberculosis or cancer. It is necessary to treat these patients with amphotericin B, as nystatin does not reach tissues.

321. The answer is B. *(Davis, ed 2. pp 986, 998.)* *Rhizopus* and *Mucor* have large hyphae, (up to 15 µ in diameter), which are nonseptate, in contrast to the hyphae of *Aspergillus*, which are 3-4 µ in diameter, septate, and show dichotomous branching. *B. dermatitidis* is a thick-walled, multi-nucleated, spherical cell 8-10 µ in diameter, without a capsule when seen on tissue section. *H. capsulatum* is a small oval yeast cell 1-3 u in diameter, found within macrophages and reticuloendothelial cells of infected tissue.

322. The answer is E. *(Jawetz, ed 11. pp 259-260.)* The actinomycetes are clearly related to bacteria, but superficially resemble fungi. They possess a muramic acid-containing wall, whereas true fungi cell walls contain chitin and cellulose.

323. The answer is A. *(Davis, ed 2. pp 1004-1005.)* *T. schoenleinii* infection may cause destruction of hair follicles and permanent loss of hair. Scutula (cup-like structures) are formed by crusts around the infected follicles. *M. furfur* is a fungal skin infection producing brownish-red scaling patches on the neck, trunk, and arms. *E. floccosum* and *T. rubrum* are common causes of athletes foot. *M. canis* infects hair and skin and can be differentiated from *Trichophyton* infections by its ability to fluoresce under ultraviolet light.

324. The answer is B. *(Jawetz, ed 11. p 269.)* Histoplasmosis is an intracellular mycosis of the reticuloenthelial system. Clinical findings include lymphadenopathy, enlarged spleen and liver, high fever, and anemia. The characteristic lesion shows focal areas of necrosis in small granulomas. The small, oval, yeast-like cells are found within phagocytic cells of the infected organ system.

325. The answer is C. *(Jawetz, ed 11. p 271.)* The source of infection in coccidioidomycosis is the inhaled arthrospore. The affected patient may have either an asymptomatic respiratory infection or an influenza-like illness. Most people recover completely with symptomatic treatment and rest. Amphotericin B is the treatment of choice for disseminated coccidioidomycosis.

326. The answer is C. *(Davis, ed 2. p 989.)* Thick-walled spores, as shown in the photomicrograph, are characteristic of many fungal infections.

327. The answer is D. *(Jawetz, ed 11. p 266.)* When grown on cornmeal- or rice-Tween agar, *C. albicans* produces chlamydospores 8-12 μ in diameter and clusters of yeasts which are diagnostically characteristic. Specimens cultured on Sabouraud's glucose agar at room temperature show yeast-like cells and pseudomycelia.

328. The answer is C. *(Davis, ed 2. pp 977, 986.)* Many species of fungi can grow as yeasts or molds depending on the environment. Many, but not all fungi, grow as molds at 25° C and as yeasts at 37° C. In infected cells, they usually appear as yeasts, and when cultivated in vitro they grow as molds.

329. The answer is B. *(Jawetz, ed 11. pp 265-267, 272, 274.)* *C. neoformans* usually forms a mucoid capsule that can be detected in unstained preparations if a suitable mounting fluid is used. *C. albicans* and *B. dermatitidis* do not form capsules. *A. fumigatus* would be present as hyphae, and *G. candidum* as hyphae and dissociated cells.

330. The answer is D. *(Davis, ed 2. pp 875-876.)* The finding of yellow "sulfur granules" in an abscess indicates actinomycosis. The presence of the granules facilitates identification, but is not necessary for a diagnosis. Most actinomycotic abscesses are mixed infections, and washed "sulfur granules" may contain colonies of various bacteria, i.e., fusiform bacilli, anaerobic streptococci.

331. The answer is A. *(Jawetz, ed 11. pp 265-269.)* Sabouraud's glucose agar is the medium of choice for culturing most fungi. On Sabouraud's agar, *Candida albicans*, incubated at room temperature, grows as soft, cream-colored colonies. *Cryptococcus neoformans* is mucoid, cream-colored, and has no mycelia. White to brownish filamentous colonies are seen with *Blastomyces dermatitidis* grown at room temperature, and white, cottony colonies made up of tuberculate spores are diagnostic of *Histoplasma capsulatum*.

332. The answer is D. *(Jawetz, ed 11. p 272.)* *Geotrichum candidum* is a yeast-like fungus which may be a normal inhabitant of the mouth and gut. It produces an infection of bronchi, lungs, and mucous membranes known as geotrichosis. Clinical findings include chronic bronchitis and thrush-like lesions of the mouth. Treatment consists of oral administration of potassium iodide and topical genetian violet (one percent) for oral lesions.

333. The answer is A. *(Davis, ed 2. pp 995-996.)* *Candida,* and in particular *C. albicans,* may be found as part of the normal flora of the mouth, vagina, or gastrointestinal tract; as a pathogen, it is an opportunistic fungi. When invasive, candidiasis can be an acute or chronic infection, either localized or disseminated. During the third trimester of pregnancy and in diabetes, high sugar levels encourage vulvovaginal candidiasis.

334. The answer is A. *(Jawetz, ed 11. pp 269-270.)* *Histoplasma capsulatum* causes histoplasmosis. It is endemic in the central and eastern USA and can be isolated from soil enriched by bird feces and bat droppings. Asymptomatic infection is common with calcified foci seen in lung, spleen, and liver on x-rays. In a minority of cases, disseminated disease occurs with involvement of the reticuloendothelial system. *H. capsulatum* grows in yeast form on blood agar at $37°$ C: when incubated on Sabouraud's agar at room temperature, diagnostic tuberculate spores develop.

335. The answer is D. *(Jawetz, ed 11. pp 184, 200, 232, 269, 484.)* Granulomas caused by histoplasmosis usually contain small, oval, budding yeast forms (as shown) in phagocytic cells. Acid-fast bacilli are found in tuberculous granulomas. Pneumococcal pneumonia is a bacterial infection due to gram-positive diplococci. Nonflagellated amastigotes (oval cells with laterally placed nuclei and rod-like kinetoplasts, also known as LD bodies) are seen in infections caused by *Leishmania donovoni,* (kala-azar). *Borrelia recurrentis* is a spirochete, which can be isolated from spleen, liver, blood, and kidneys.

336. The answer is C. *(Davis, ed 2. p 981.)* Supporting evidence of fungal infections includes the clinical appearance of lesions and positive serologic reactions. Detection of fungi in lesions, however, either by microscopic inspection or culture, is the best evidence. A 10% percent solution of NaOH or KOH hydrolyzes protein, fat, and many polysaccharides, and leaves the cell walls of most fungi intact and visible due to their alkali-resistant glucans.

337. The answer is C. *(Jawetz, ed 11. pp 262-264.)* The dermatophytes are a group of fungi that infect only superficial keratinized tissue (skin, hair, nails). They form hyphae and arthrospores on the skin, and in culture develop colonies and spore forms. Tinea pedis, or athlete's foot, is the most common dermatophytosis. Several topical antifungal agents are useful in treatment, i.e., undecylenic acid, salicylic acid, ammoniated mercury. In serious infection, systemic use of griseofulvin is effective.

338. The answer is E. *(Davis, ed 2. pp 986, 988, 990, 997, 1000.)* *H. capsulatum* and *C. neoformans* are quite commonly isolated from soil contaminated with bird droppings, but are not usually present in fresh droppings. The droppings' function is, therefore, thought to be enrichment of soil or other substances as a culture medium. Birds are highly resistant to both these organisms which can remain viable in dried material for months. *S. schenckii* grows in soil and on vegetation, and the distribution of *B. dermatitis* is not known, although it may be soil or organic debris.

339. The answer is A. *(Davis, ed 2. pp 999-1000.)* The most common form of sporotrichosis involves the lymphatics which drain the primary lesion. The classic syndrome is a chronic ulcer on a finger or hand, and an associated chain of enlarged lymph nodes extending up the arm. If untreated, the mycosis may disseminate.

340. The answer is E (all). *(Davis, ed 2. pp 998-1000.)* Mucormycosis, also called phycomycosis, is commonly caused by *Mucor* and *Rhizopus* species. Inhalation of spores causes an infection that is most often seen in diabetic, uremic, and immunosuppressed hosts. Large hyphae extend through contiguous tissues and produce angiitis, thrombi, and necrosis. Clinical lesions are dark in appearance (brown to black) and commonly seen in the oral pharynx.

341. The answer is E (all). *(Jawetz, ed 11. pp 270-271.)* Coccidioidomycosis is a fungal disease, endemic in the southwestern USA. Patients inhale arthrospores which can cause either an asymptomatic respiratory infection or an influenza-like illness. Fewer than five percent of these individuals subsequently develop a hypersensitivity reaction which manifests as erythema nodosum or multiforme. This symptomatology is then termed "valley fever" or "desert rheumatism," in which thin-walled cavities may appear in the lungs. All these symptoms tend to subside spontaneously. In less than one percent of patients, disseminated disease occurs, with granulomas indistinguishable from tuberculosis seen in all organs.

342. The answer is D (4). *(Davis, ed 2. p 993. Jawetz, ed 11. p 271.)* Precipitin titers usually disappear after the fourth week of coccidioidomycosis. Complement-fixing IgG antibodies may not appear in mild disease, and become positive in high titer only in disseminated disease, indicating a poor prognosis. A positive skin test to coccidioidin appears 2-21 days after the appearance of disease symptoms and may persist for 20 years without re-exposure to the fungus. A decrease in intensity of the skin response often occurs in clinically healthy people who move away from endemic areas. A negative skin test is often found in association with disseminated disease.

343. The answer is C (2, 4). *(Davis, ed 2. pp 997-998, 1002-1003.)* In general, only a few fungal diseases are contagious, including certain of the dermatophytoses. Candidiasis of the newborn can, however, be acquired from the birth canal, although in most instances it is due to an increased susceptibility to a member of the normal human flora. The agent of actinomycosis is a normal inhabitant of the oral cavity. Most of the systemic mycoses are caused by fungi which grow as free-living saprophytes in the soil. Humans and other animals are, in general, only accidental hosts and are not required to maintain the life cycle of fungi.

344. The answer is A (1, 2, 3). *(Davis, ed 2. p 980.)* Fungi are eukaryotic, while bacteria are prokaryotic. Fungi are sensitive to griseofulvin, while bacteria are not. Bacteria's cell walls contain peptidoglycan, and their membranes lack sterols, in contrast to fungi.

345. The answer is E (all). *(Davis, ed 2. pp 984-985.)* The characteristic capsules of cryptococci allow the yeast cells to be easily seen in India ink suspensions. All strains of cryptococci produce capsules, but only *C. neoformans* is pathogenic in humans. Although infected humans have only a weak immune response, hyperimmunized rabbits produce capsule-specific antisera which differentiates three strains. The precipitin reaction with rabbit serum is the only serologic test of diagnostic value.

346. The answer is E (all). *(Davis, ed 2. p 979.)* Cutaneous mycoses (dermatophytes) and superficial mycoses cause disease in skin, hair, and nails by invasion of keratinized skin. Systemic fungal disease is caused by inhalation of spores. Infections due to direct implantation of spores in the skin, called subcutaneous mycoses, are caused by soil saprophytes. Fungi of normal flora can directly invade a susceptible host through mucous membranes and cause local or disseminated disease (vulvovaginal candidiasis in pregnancy and diabetes).

347. The answer is E (all). *(Davis, ed 2. pp 971-972.)* Budding is the major asexual reproductive process that occurs in yeasts. Other forms of vegetative reproduction which occur in fungi include sporulation followed by germination, and fragmentation of hyphae. These methods yield new clones without nuclear fusion. Sexual reproduction with fusion of donor and recipient cell nuclei allows for genetic variation among the four haploid cells that are formed.

348-351. The answers are: 348-B, 349-A, 350-D, 351-E. *(Jawetz, ed 11. p 142.)* Certain underlying constitutional diseases or conditions have an increased association with particular supervening infections; this is in part due to hormonal and drug influences. In addition to the associations mentioned, the following ones frequently occur: sickle cell trait and pneumococcal bacteremia; cirrhosis or nephrosis and pneumococcal peritonitis; diabetes mellitus and mucormycosis and candidiasis; immunosuppression by drugs and many "opportunistic" infections.

352-356. The answers are: 352-D, 353-E, 354-C, 355-A, 356-B.
(Jawetz, ed 11. pp 263-264.) *N. minutissima* causes erythrasmas, a superficial skin infection. Piedra is an infection in which soft, white nodules are found attached to the hair, caused by *T. beigelii*. Tinea capitis is ringworm of the scalp due to infection with *M. gypseum*. It usually occurs during childhood and heals spontaneously at puberty. Athlete's foot (tinea pedis) is a common dermatophytic infection, of which *E. floccosum* is often the causative fungi. Tinea versicolor consists of white or tan scales on the trunk, and is caused by *M. furfur*.

Parasitology

357. The answer is C. *(Brown, ed 4. pp 97-98.)* The large reservoir of malarial disease in the United States was eliminated by vigorous treatment of all human cases combined with effective mosquito control.

358. The answer is B. *(Jawetz, ed 11. p 482. Teplick, ed 2. p 259.)* *Giardia lamblia* infests the duodenum and jejunum but rarely the terminal ileum.

359. The answer is E. *(Brown, ed 4. p 1.)* Facultative parasites are capable of sustaining growth on their own in an extracellular environment or within a cell. Obligate parasites must reside on or within another living organism for growth and reproduction. A pseudoparasite is not a true parasite, but an artifact that is mistaken for one.

360. The answer is A. *(Jawetz, ed 11. pp 488-490.)* The most pathogenic ameboid intestinal protozoa is *Entamoeba histolytica*, a common parasite found in the large intestine of humans. *Dientamoeba fragilis* is also an intestinal ameba thought to produce mild diarrhea and dyspepsia. *Trichomonas hominis* is a flagellate protozoa, and is generally considered to be harmless.

361. The answer is D. *(Brown, ed 4. pp 146-147. Jawetz, ed 11. pp 496, 505.)* Filariasis, also known as elephantiasis and wuchereriasis is caused by extensive growth and proliferation of *Wuchereria bancrofti*. The parasite is transmitted through the bite of mosquitoes, and humans are the only definitive host. Microfilariae are commonly found in blood and observed in smears.

362. The answer is A. *(Brown, ed 4. p 195. Faust, ed 8. pp 545-550.)* The adult form of *E. granulosus* lives in the intestine of dogs, wolves, foxes, and other carnivores. Humans become infected by ingesting eggs of the parasite. The eggs hatch in the intestines and migrate to lungs and liver. It is in these areas that the characteristic hydatid cysts forms.

363. The answer is A. *(Brown, ed 4. p 111. Faust, ed 8. p 271.)* A specific diagnosis of infection with *Trichinella spiralis* can be made by demonstration of larvae in muscle by biopsy. Examination of feces for the adult worm and of blood, spinal fluid, and other exudates for larvae is usually negative. Intradermal and complement-fixation tests are not completely accurate. Eosinophilia, myositis, and periorbital edema are important diagnostic clues in this disease.

364. The answer is B. *(Brown, ed 4. pp 226-230. Jawetz, ed 11. pp 496, 506-507.)* The Chinese liver fluke, *Clonorchis sinensis*, is a parasite of humans found in Japan, China, South Korea, Formosa, and Vietnam. Humans are usually infected by eating uncooked fish. The worms invade bile ducts and produce destruction of liver parenchyma. Anemia, jaundice, weakness, weight loss, and tachycardia may follow. Treatment is usually not satisfactory in heavy infections, but chloroquine will destroy some of the worms.

365. The answer is C. *(Brown, ed 4. pp 226-227.)* The life cycle of *Clonorchis sinensis* is similar to that of other trematodes and requires a mollusk as the first intermediate host; in this case, it is the snail.

366. The answer is E. *(Brown, ed 4. p 132. Faust, ed 8. pp 330-334.)* Pinworm, *Enterobius vermicularis*, is a parasite of the cecum and intestine. At night, female worms migrate to deposit eggs in perianal and perineal regions. While fecal specimens are frequently unrewarding, good recovery of eggs can be obtained by perianal swabs with cellophane tape. The eggs adhere to the tape and can be identified microscopically. Consecutive swabbing for three days will reveal 90 percent of infections.

367. The answer is E. *(Brown, ed 4. pp 125-126. Faust, ed 8. pp 42-43, 308-309.)* *Necator americanus* and *Ancylostoma duodenale* are responsible for most human hookworm infections. Filariform larvae of these organisms gain access to humans by penetration of the skin, usually through the interdigital spaces between the toes of barefoot people. Damp, loosely packed soil, warm climate, accessibility of fecal matter, and bare feet are the major factors responsible for the spread of hookworms.

368. The answer is C. *(Brown, ed 4. p 119. Faust, ed 8. p 287.)* Strongyloides is a common intestinal parasite in tropical areas. The rhabditiform larvae of *S. stercoralis* may develop into infective filariform larvae in transit down the bowel and produce reinfection by invading the mucosa of the lower portion of the colon. Because of autoinfection, strongyloidiasis may persist for years if untreated.

369. The answer is D. *(Brown, ed 4. pp 54-58. Faust, ed 8. pp 117-119.)* *Trypanosoma cruzi*, the cause of Chagas' disease, can be transmitted by 28 species of reduviid bug, but the principal vector is *Triatoma*. The bug often defecates while biting, and the fecal material containing the infective metacyclic stage of trypanosome contaminates the bite. Blood transfusions can also be a source of infection. At present, there is no really effective treatment available for Chagas' disease.

370. The answer is C. *(Brown, ed 4. pp 162-163. Faust, ed 8. pp 344-345.)* In an unnatural host (humans) the larvae of the dog ascarid (*Toxocara canis*) and the cat ascarid (*T. cati*) are unable to complete their normal development. Instead, they migrate extensively through extraintestinal viscera until they are stopped by a host cell response which isolates them in granulomas. Lesions containing *toxocara* larva have been found in the eye, brain, liver, kidney, lungs, and lymph nodes.

371. The answer is B. *(Faust, ed 8. pp 529-538.)* Both beef tapeworm (*Taenia saginata*) and pork tapeworm (*T. solium*) can, in the adult form, cause disturbances of intestinal function. This is due both to direct irritation and to metabolic toxic wastes. In addition, *T. saginata*, because of its large size, may produce acute intestinal blockage. *T. solium* can be particularly dangerous because unlike *T. saginata* (in which the cysticercus stage develops only in cattle) it produces cysticercosis that results in serious lesions in humans.

372. The answer is D. *(Brown, ed 4. pp 310-314.)* Spiders are injurious to humans only through the action of their venomous stings. The most dangerous species, *Lactrodectus mactans* the black widow, and *Loxosceles reclusa* the brown recluse, can occasionally cause death, chiefly in children. *Loxosceles* in addition to producing severe necrotic lesions, can sometimes cause a syndrome of hematuria, anemia, fever, and convulsions.

373. The answer is C. *(Brown, ed 4. p 214.)* In the typical life cycle of trematodes, eggs are discharged via the intestinal or genitourinary tract of a definitive host. In fresh water, the egg hatches, releasing the larval miracidium which enters an appropriate snail as an intermediate host. Metamorphosis then takes place forming rediae which develop into cercariae. The cercariae are released from the intermediate host and re-enter the water. Encysted, metacercariae must be ingested by humans: cercariae can penetrate their skin. The schizont is an asexual form of the malarial protozoans.

374. The answer is B. *(Brown, ed 4. pp 14-98.)* The protozoans that infect humans include: amebas, *Entamoeba coli*; flagellates, *G. lamblia*; trypanosomes, *Leishmania donovani*; sporozoans, *P. vivax*; and other protozoan forms of uncertain nature, *P. carinii*. *E. granulosus* is a tapeworm which causes hydatid disease in humans.

375. The answer is E. *(Brown, 4th ed. pp 4-8, 209, 231.)* Helminths are subdivided into three phyla: the Annelida or segmented worms; the Nemathelminthes or roundworms; and the Platyhelminthes or flatworms. Platyhelminthes are subdivided into Cestoda or tapeworms, such as *D. latum* and *T. saginata,* and the Trematoda or flukes, such as *F. hepatica* and *S. mansoni*. *Ascaris lumbricoides* is a roundworm.

376. The answer is A. *(Brown, ed 4. pp 121-126.)* Adult hookworms, aided by the secretion of an anticoagulant, ingest blood from hosts. The last three statements listed are true of the infectious filariform larva, but not of the adult worm which must mature in the gut.

377. The answer is B. *(Brown, ed 4. pp 8-9, 54, 94, 108, 131.)* Pinworm is a widespread and exceedingly common disease: Surveys in Washington, D. C. show a 12 to 41 percent infection rate. While trichinosis still has a cosmopolitan distribution, it now affects not more than 2.2 percent of the American population compared to 15-25 percent 35 years ago. Schistosomiasis and trypanosomiasis are, for the most part, limited to Africa, South America, and Asia. Malaria is common to most tropical and subtropical countries.

378. The answer is D. *(Brown, ed 4. pp 40-41.)* The organism shown is too small for a worm and too large for a bacterium. It is the trophozoite form of *Giardia lamblia.* Giardiasis can cause acute diarrhea, abdominal pain, and weight loss. It is spread through contaminated food or water.

379. The answer is B. *(Brown, ed 4. p 137.)* Piperazine citrate and other piperazine salts have become the drugs of choice in the treatment of roundworms such as *Ascaris.* The drugs are safe, and 95 percent effective when administered on two consecutive days. They act by relaxing worm musculature, causing the worm to be eliminated by normal peristaltic action.

380. The answer is B. *(Brown, ed 4. pp 182, 191.)* Niclosamide is the drug of choice for treatment of infection with several tapeworm species, including *Taenia saginata* and *Diphyllobothrium latum.* It is also effective against *Taenia solium*, but in this case must be used with a saline purge and an antiemetic to avoid cysticercosis. Quinacrine hydrocholoride is effective for treatment of tapeworms, but frequently causes vomiting.

381. The answer is D. *(Brown, ed 4. pp 105-141, 178-194.)* *Enterobius* (pinworm), *Ascaris* (roundworm), *Necator* (hookworm), and *Trichuris* (whipworm) are roundworms or nematodes. *Taenia saginata* (tapeworm) is a cestode or flatworm.

382. The answer is C. *(Brown, ed 4. pp 61-62. Jawetz, ed 11. pp 484 485.)* *Leishmania donovani*, the causative agent of kala-azar spreads from the site of inoculation and multiplies in the reticuloendothelial cells, especially in macrophages of the spleen, lymph nodes, and bone marrow. Blood is usually examined first, when the disease is suspected, but splenic punctures have a much higher percentage of positive findings and are the method of choice in skilled hands. Biopsies of liver, lymph nodes, and bone marrow are also useful diagnostic tests and although less accurate safer procedures.

383. The answer is E. *(Brown, ed 4. p 68. Jawetz, ed 11. p 998.)* Toxoplasmosis is a disease caused by *Toxoplasma gondii*, a protozoan of worldwide distribution. Although infection with this organism is common, (up to 80 percent in some populations) disease is rare. It is transmitted through raw meat or cats via oocysts in their feces. Congenital disease may be acquired in utero.

384. The answer is D. *(Brown, ed 4. p 142. Jawetz, ed 11. p 500.)* The microfilariae are parasitic nematodes of the blood and lymphatics. *W. bancrofti*, the best known member of this group, frequently causes inflammation of the lymphatics, terminating in obstructive edema and elephantiasis. *Schistosoma haematobium* is a trematode, not a microfilariae.

385. The answer is A. *(Brown, ed 4. pp 82-83, 88-89.)* The febrile paroxysms of malariae malaria occur at intervals of 72 hours, of falciparum and vivax malaria at intervals of 48 hours. The paroxysms usually last only 8 to 12 hours with vivax, but can last 16 to 36 hours with falciparum. In malignant tertian (*P. falciparum*) infections only early ring stages and gametocytes are usually found in the peripheral blood; in vivax, ovale, and malariae all stages of development are seen.

386. The answer is C. *(Brown, ed 4. pp 179-181. Jawetz, ed 11. p 497.)* *Diphyllobothrium latum* is commonly transmitted to man via infected fresh-water fish. The parasite can now be found on virtually every continent. *T. saginata* is transmitted in uncooked beef. *H. diminuta* is spread by infected insects. Free living forms of *Strongyloides* and *Schistosoma* directly penetrate the skin of their hosts.

387. The answer is B. *(Brown, ed 4. pp 79, 82.)* The patient described is infected with *Plasmodium falciparum*. The long duration of the febrile stage rules out other forms of malaria. The ring form trophozoites, crescent form gametocytes, and the absence of schizonts shown in illustration B are diagnostic of falciparum malaria.

388. The answer is E (all). *(Brown, ed 4. pp 109-110.)* The clinical course of trichinosis progresses through three phases which correspond to stages in the life cycle of the infecting organism. First, there is intestinal invasion by adult worms clinically manifested by diarrhea and abdominal pain. Second, there is migration of the larvae accompanied by muscle pain, eosinophilia and edema. Finally, with encystment of the parasite, there is weakness and fatigue.

389. The answer is E (all). *(Brown, ed 4. p 318.)* Too much emphasis is sometimes placed on eosinophilia as a definite sign of parasitic disease. Eosinophilia is found in a variety of diseases including all of those listed, as well as asthma, gonorrhea, herpes zoster and many others. Eosinophilia is not even a consistent sign of parasitic disease: The degree of eosinophilia varies with both host response and duration of infection.

390. The answer is D (4). *(Brown, ed 4. pp 245, 252-254.)* *Schistosoma mansoni* (dysentery) occurs in Africa, South America, Puerto Rico, and several other islands. *S. japonicum* (oriental) is confined to the Far East. *S. haematobium* (hematuria) is distributed through Africa and the Middle East. On the other hand, schistosome cercariae of nonhuman hosts cause a dermatitis among swimmers on both coasts of the United States and in many lakes throughout the country.

391. The answer is B (1, 3). *(Brown, ed 4. pp 268-270.)* Bedbugs are bloodsucking parasites of man. At night they leave their hiding places to feed on humans and small mammals. Their bite produces red itching wheals in characteristic groups of two. The bugs have not proved to be vectors of human disease, and DDT applied to furniture and mattresses can control them.

392. The answer is E (all). *(Brown, ed 4. pp 260-262.)* Lice are wingless insects. *Pediculus humanus* (head and body lice) and *Phthirus pubis* (crab louse) are exclusive parasites of humans. Lice are important not only for the itching and discomfort that they cause, but for the diseases they transmit.

393. The answer is A (1, 2, 3). *(Brown, ed 4. pp 68-69.)* Serologic tests, such as the Sabin-Feldman dye test, have shown that a high percentage of the world's population has been infected with *Toxoplasma gondii*. In adults, clinical toxoplasmosis usually presents as a benign infectious mononucleosis-like syndrome. On the other hand, in fetal infections it is often severe, accompanied by hydrocephalus, chorioretinitis, and convulsions, and can lead to death.

394. The answer is E (all). *(Brown, ed 4. pp 307-309.)* *Sarcoptes scabiei* is a small mite which burrows into the skin, especially of the hands, wrist, groin, and back. The mites cause itching and a vesicular eruption which often becomes secondarily infected with bacteria. Diagnosis is made by microscopic examination of the mites. Kwell, a topical insecticide, is an effective treatment.

395. The answer is C (2, 4). *(Ishikawa, J Cell Biol 43:312. Wilson, 1973. pp 531-533.)* The fibers shown are similar to muscle actin and are involved in cellular motility.

396. The answer is B (1, 3). *(Brown, ed 4. pp 195-202.)* The hydatid is the cysticercus form of the flatworm *Echinococcus granulosus*. The adult worm is harbored in the small intestine of dogs, coyotes, and other intermediates. Eggs are transmitted to humans in the feces of these intermediates. Echinococcosis is a rare infection, typically involving the liver, and less commonly the brain, lungs, or bones.

397. The answer is C (2, 4). *(Brown, ed 4. pp 209-254. Wintrobe, ed 7. pp 1048-1054.)* Trematode infections are rare in the United States, (fewer than ten cases per year) and treatment of them is difficult and nonspecific. (Thiabendazole is an antinematode drug.) The intermediate host of the trematodes is, typically, a single crustacean in the case of schistosomes, and two crustaceans (or a crustacean and aquatic vegetation) in the case of the hermaphroditic flukes.

398. The answer is E (all). *(Brown, ed 4. pp 105-112, 187-193. Jawetz, ed 11. p 98. Wintrobe, ed 7. pp 852-855, 1055-1057.)* *Clostridium perfringens* food poisoning is transmitted overwhelmingly by insufficiently cooked meat that is stored at ambient temperatures. The pork and beef tapeworms, as well as *Trichinella spiralis*, all spend a portion of their life cycle encysted in the tissues of a secondary host and are infectious if not killed by freezing or heating before eating.

399. The answer is B (1, 3). *(Brown, ed 4. pp 133-137, 162-164.)* The liver flukes, so named because of their predisposition for biliary infestation, include *Echinococcus*, *Clonorchis*, *Fasciola*, and *Opisthorchis*. Paragonimiasis is chiefly a pulmonary fluke infestation, in which fibrosis is elicited and hemoptysis is a cardinal sign. Ascariasis is chiefly an intestinal disease in humans, which in the bulk of patients is only minimally symptomatic: When ascaris worms migrate, they can elicit eosinophilia, infest liver and lungs, and emerge from the upper airway, causing aspiration.

400. The answer is B (1, 3). *(Brown, ed 4. pp 75-98.)* Plasmodia are ameboid intracellular parasites that infect erythrocytes and produce a normocytic anemia. Chloroquine is the drug of choice for acute attacks. Primaquine, by contrast, has its chief use in prophylaxis and relapse prevention (after radical cure). The schizogonic or asexual life cycle of malarial plasmodia occurs in the red cells of vertebrates including humans. The sporogonic or sexual life cycle of the malarial parasite occurs in anopheline mosquitoes.

401. The answer is D (4). *(Brown, ed 4. pp 283-284.)* Sandfly fever is a mild viral disease carried by the fly *Phlebotomus papatasii* that produces a pruritic, rose-colored papular eruption which lasts approximately one week. The prodrome of the illness includes abrupt onset of headache, fever, malaise, and arthralgia. Viremia occurs 24 hours before the onset of symptoms and lasts for 48 hours. The illness is not treatable with antibiotics. Sandfly fever is prevalent in Mediterranean countries and in southern Asia. Bartonellosis occurs in South America as acute febrile Carrión's disease and as a chronic granulomatous condition, and is transmitted by the Andean sandfly.

402. The answer is A (1, 2, 3). *(Brown, ed 4. pp 176-177.)* Disease produced by adult cestodes is not usually clinically significant. Minor clinical disturbances such as weakness, fatigue, and irritability may result from the mechanisms outlined in answers one through three. Infrequently, the worms can cause intestinal obstruction or perforation when present in great bulk.

403. The answer is A (1, 2, 3). *(Jawetz, ed 11. p 482.)* *Giardia lamblia* is a flagellated protozoan found in the duodenum and jejunum of humans, which may cause flagellate diarrhea or giardiasis, but is often nonpathogenic. Mild cholecystitis may occur in cases where the bile ducts and the gallbladder are invaded. Treatment with quinacrine hydrochloride (Atabrine) or metronidazole (Flagyl) is curative in the majority of clinically significant cases.

404. The answer is D (4). *(Jawetz, ed 11. p 483.)* Of the three species of *Trichomonas* which may inhabit humans, *T. tenax* is found in the mouth, *T. hominis* in the intestine, and *T. vaginalis* in the genitourinary tract. *T. hominis* and *T. tenax* are considered nonpathogenic, whereas *T. vaginalis* is responsible for vaginal (but not uterine) infections in women, and prostatic as well as urethral infections in men. Transmission of *T. vaginalis* occurs during coitus. Trichomoniasis in both women and men can be cured by administration of systemic metronidazole (Flagyl).

405. The answer is A (1, 2, 3). *(Brown, ed 4. pp 75-98. Jawetz, ed 11. p 492.)* The length of the asexual cycle of *P. vivax, P. ovale,* and *P. falciparum* is 48 hours or less. In the case of *P. malariae*, 72 hours is required for the reproduction of merozoites. The periodicity of chills, fever, nausea, and vomiting in malarial infections corresponds to the end of the schizogonic cycle, when merozoites of the mature schizonts rupture into the circulation; this occurs every other day with *P. vivax, P. ovale,* and *P. falciparum,* and every 72 hours with *P. malariae.*

406. The answer is E (all). *(Brown, ed 4. pp 129-133.)* Pinworm infections are innocuous and usually self-limited, though common. The disease is found mostly in children, but may be spread to other household members. Treatment with pyrantel pamoate or piperazine is given to the entire family of an affected child for this reason.

407. The answer is E (all). *(Brown, ed 4. pp 239-252. Wintrobe, ed 7. pp 1048-1052.)* Although the chronic stage of proliferation within tissue is distinctive in the different forms of schistosomiasis, in all forms there is a granulomatous reaction to the eggs and chemical products of the schistosome that occurs at the loci of oviposition. *Schistosoma haematobium* commonly involves the distal bowel and the bladder, as well as prostate and seminal vesicles; bladder calcification and cancer may ensue. *S. mansoni* involves the large bowel and the liver; pre-sinusoidal portal hypertension, splenomegaly, and esophageal varices may be complications. In the several forms of schistosomiasis, rectal biopsy, with examination of the unstained mucosa for eggs, or stool examinations may be positive. In the specific forms mentioned above, urine microscopy and liver biopsy often prove positive. Pulmonary hypertension, often fatal, may be seen with *S. mansoni* and *S. japonicum*. Treatment of the various forms of schistosomiasis with arsenicals or niridazole has major toxicities and limitations and is less satisfactory than control of the disease by elimination of the parasite in snails, before human infection occurs.

408. The answer is A (1, 2, 3). *(Jawetz, ed 11. pp 488, 490.)* *Entamoeba histolytica* is an intestinal parasite of humans. It usually causes asymptomatic infections, but may cause amebic dysentery. The cysts of *E. histolytica* may be seen even in the stool of asymptomatic patients. However, dysentery and symptoms of amebiasis occur only after trophozoites invade the intestinal mucosa, and at that time trophozoites will also appear in the stool.

409. The answer is D (4). *(Jawetz, ed 11. pp 491-492.)* Malaria involves a sporogonic sexual cycle which takes place in the female *Anopheles* mosquito, and a schizogonic asexual cycle which takes place in humans. The first phase of the human infection is pre-erythrocytic, occurring in the liver parenchyma and yielding merozoites which enter the blood stream, and infest erythrocytes. Certain species of plasmodia have predilections for red cells of certain ages, but *P. falciparum* invades red cells of all ages and is the most severe type of malaria for this reason. Typically, there is coarse stippling of parasitized cells with *P. falciparum*, and fine stippling of parasitized cells with *P. vivax* and *P. ovale*.

410. The answer is A (1, 2, 3). *(Jawetz, ed 11. p 486.)* American trypanosomiasis, Chagas' disease, is produced by *Trypanosoma cruzi*, which is transmitted to humans in the feces of the reduviid bug percutaneously or via the conjunctiva; inoculation by the latter route may result in Romaña's sign, unilateral eyelid swelling. Hepatosplenomegaly results from infection involving the reticuloendothelial system; interstitial myocarditis results from involvement of the heart and may cause congestive heart failure. African trypanosomiasis, or sleeping sickness, is caused by *T. gambiense* or *T. rhodesiense*, is transmitted by the tsetse fly, and yields greater parasitemia than *T. cruzi*.

411. The answer is B (1, 3). *(Jawetz, ed 11. pp 488-491.)* Amebic infestation of the human intestine is often asymptomatic. Symptomatic amebiasis and dysentery result when ameboid trophozoites invade the intestinal wall, producing ulcers, diarrhea, and occasionally extraintestinal involvement, e.g., hepatic and brain abscess. Amebic disease is usually transmitted by the cyst form of the organism.

Immunology

412. The answer is A. *(Davis, ed 2. pp 456, 572-573.)* Antibody is formed and secreted chiefly by plasma cells, and cells which arise from bone marrow derived lymphocytes (B cells). Thymus-derived lymphocytes elaborate the other cited factors, as well as a number of less well defined stimulatory and suppressive factors. The T cell is thus best considered as the regulator cell of the immune system.

413. The answer is D. *(Gell, ed 3. pp 103-104.)* Each immunoglobulin class has a biochemically different type of heavy chain which is responsible for antigenic differences observed between classes. The light chains are common to the various immunoglobulin classes, and the secretory component is a fragment added to IgA in specialized epithelial cells. The J chain is a component of IgM and IgA multimers.

414. The answer is D. *(Davis, ed 2. pp 506-507.)* Live vaccines, including BCG attenuated from *M. tuberculosis*, should not be used in the clinical evaluation of immune competence, since individuals with severe deficiencies may suffer overwhelming infections. For the same reason, oral (Sabin) polio vaccine is not advisable in such patients.

415. The answer is C. *(Gell, ed 3. p 298.)* Bence Jones proteins are homogenous free globulin light chains present in the urine of about 50 percent of patients with multiple myeloma. They are not albumin, nor are they always detectable by the "dip-test" reagents often employed to monitor urine for albumin. Mu and gamma chains are types of heavy chains.

416. The answer is D. *(Davis, ed 2. pp 1346-1347. Gell, ed 3. pp 1004-1005.)* Measles virus, or a virus identical to it, has been isolated from the brains of patients with subacute sclerosing panencephalitis. Immunofluorescence studies have demonstrated antigens reactive with measles antibody, and patients with the disease also have high titers of measles antibody.

417. The answer is E. *(Davis, ed 2. pp 1314-1317.)* Antibodies formed against the nucleocapsid, nucleoprotein, and M protein will not neutralize the infectivity of influenza virus. Antibody against neuraminidase will not prevent infection but will reduce viral spread from infected cells. The hemagglutinin on the virion's surface, which corresponds to the "spikes" seen by electron microscopy on the virion, is the major target of neutralizing antibody. M protein and nucleocapsid antigens provide the basis for typing of influenza virus.

418. The answer is A. *(Gell, ed 3. p 135.)* The virus neutralization test will detect as little as 1×10^{-4} mg of antibody nitrogen per test. Complement fixation and radioimmunoassay are highly sensitive tests and are much more sensitive than the immunodiffusion and immunoelectrophoretic assays.

419. The answer is A. *(Gell, ed 3. pp 419-420, 480, 1388-1390.)* IgA is the principal immunoglobulin in exocrine secretions, and provides most of the humoral protection against pathogens which invade the mucosal surfaces of the respiratory, intestinal, and genitourinary tracts. IgA is a multimeric antibody which contains a "secretory piece" elaborated by specialized epithelial cells.

420. The answer is B. *(Davis, ed 2. pp 546-551, 638. Gell, ed 3. p 1640.)* Inactivated vaccine stimulates the formation of high levels of serum antibodies that form complexes with live viruses resulting in the accumulation of humoral and cellular factors which mediate the immunologic tissue injury of the Arthus reaction. The Prausnitz-Küstner reaction concerns passively transferred antibody later challenged intradermally with antigen. The Shwartzman reaction is a two-step, cutaneous response to bacterial endotoxin. The Schick reaction is elicited with intradermal diphtheria toxin, and used to assay immunity to diphtheria. The Coombs reaction is an antiglobulin test used in vitro to demonstrate the presence of red cell antibodies.

421. The answer is E. *(Davis, ed 2. pp 517-519. Gell, ed 3. pp 323-364.)* All nine components of complement must interact to produce swift cell lysis. However, when all components through C8 are bound, functional membrane lesions develop which on incubation at $37°$ C may lead to slow lysis. Binding of C9 to the foregoing complex accelerates lysis and produces circular membrane lesions similar to those produced by detergent polyene antibiotics.

422. The answer is B. *(Davis, ed 2. p 610.)* Isografts are grafts between genetically identical individuals. Autografts are transplants from one region to another on the same individual. Homografts are transplants from a genetically nonidentical individual of the same species. Heterografts (or xenografts) are transplants from one species to another.

423. The answer is B. *(Davis, ed 2. pp 538-551.)* The Arthus reaction is a classic inflammatory response, involving a cellular infiltrate provoked by antigen and antibody in much larger quantities (by a factor of 10^5) than those required for passive cutaneous anaphylaxis. Whereas the edema of cutaneous anaphylaxis appears within 10 minutes and resolves within 30 minutes of antigen injection, the polymorphonuclear leukocyte infiltrate of an Arthus reaction appears after more than one hour, peaks at three to four hours, and resolves within 12 hours. Serum sickness is an immune complex disease that follows exposure to antigen by one to two weeks, and involves fever, lymphadenopathy, arthralgia, and a generalized systemic response to circulating immune complexes.

424. The answer is D. *(Beeson, ed 14. pp 1474-1479.)* A metabolic abnormality in the leukocytes of individuals with chronic granulomatous disease leads to defective intracellular killing of catalase-positive bacteria of low virulence. Leukocytes in affected patients fail to exhibit a post-phagocytic burst of oxygen consumption and glucose metabolism. Ultimately they fail to produce hydrogen peroxide, and compromise myeloperoxidase-halogenation mechanisms used to kill bacteria in leukocytes.

425. The answer is E. *(Gell, ed 3. pp 295-296, 301, 497-498, 1005.)* The gamma globulin in the blood of an infant until the second or third month postpartum is predominately IgG, passively acquired from the mother. The fetus responds to in utero infection with antibody production of the IgM class, which is ontogenically the earliest antibody form in evolution.

426. The answer is C. *(Jawetz, ed 11. p 149.)* The heavy and light chains of immunoglobulin molecules M and G are covalently linked by disulfide bonds which can be broken by mild reduction. The light chains of IgA_2 are associated noncovalently with the heavy chains.

427. The answer is B. *(Jawetz, ed 11. p 230.)* The Wassermann and Kolmer tests for syphilis are complement-fixation tests based on the fact that sera containing antitreponemal antibody fix complement in the presence of cardiolipin antigen. The tests become positive after the second or third week of infection in serum or after the fourth to eighth week of infection in the spinal fluid.

428. The answer is B. *(Davis, ed 2. pp 529-530, 538.)* Anaphylaxis is initiated by antigen-antibody complexes which trigger release mechanisms of mast cells, basophils, and in some species, platelets. These yield vasoactive amines including histamine and serotonin, as well as various kinins, which act to dilate blood vessels and contract smooth muscle in anaphylaxis. Since Dale discovered in 1911 that injections of histamine could duplicate the experimental picture of anaphylaxis, histamine has remained a major factor in anaphylaxis as it is seen in humans, dogs, rabbits, and guinea pigs, but not in rats and mice.

429. The answer is C. *(Davis, ed 2. p 530.)* The passive transfer of cutaneous anaphylaxis in humans, known as the Prausnitz-Küstner reaction, classically requires a latent period of 10 to 20 hours for sensitization to occur. From one day to as long as six weeks after injection of antibody, the corresponding antigen can elicit a wheal-and-flare response.

430. The answer is C. *(Williams, 1972. pp 1046-1047.)* The fact that in asplenic subjects no platelets are lost rapidly from the circulation, indicates the spleen's involvment with platelet monitoring. Newly produced platelets also spend several days localized in the spleen.

431. The answer is D. *(Williams, 1972. pp 1046-1049.)* Intravenous infusion of epinephrine reduces the blood pool in the spleen, causing the spleen to empty passively into the circulation. Epinephrine thereby increases, by approximately 30 percent, the circulating platelet count.

432. The answer is C. *(Davis, ed 2. p 477.)* Gut-associated lymphatic aggregates (lymphoepithelial structures) form a system which includes the tonsils, appendix, and Peyer's patches. In all, follicular organization follows a pattern of B cell preponderance in germinal centers, and T cell preponderance in the intervening parafollicular zones. Peyer's patches are found chiefly in the distal ileum.

433. The answer is D. *(Jawetz, ed 11. pp 148-151.)* IgG is the only immunoglobulin which crosses the placenta. Its molecular weight is only 150,000 compared with IgM (900,000) and IgA (170-400,000), which exist chiefly as multimeric forms too large to pass through the vasculature of the placental membranes. IgD and E are found normally in minute quantities in serum, and are not known to pass through the placenta, even though their molecular weights are 180-200,000, and they exist as monomers.

434. The answer is C. *(Jawetz, ed 11. p 164.)* Histamine is released from mast cells and is released from platelets during anaphylaxis. Kinins, especially bradykinin, are increased during anaphylaxis. SRS-A in lipoprotein is of uncertain origin, and is also released in anaphylaxis. Although some prostaglandins and other mediators appear to have roles in anaphylaxis, endogenous pyrogen does not appear to be one of these; anaphylaxis is associated more often with hypotension, hypothermia, and cool shock, than with hyperthermia.

435. The answer is E. *(Davis, ed 2. p 419. Gell, ed 3. pp 1101-1105.)* Rheumatoid factors are known to be immunoglobulins, usually IgM and less often IgG, which can react with other immunoglobulins. Many of these sera identify allotypic makers on other IgGs, and have been used to elucidate the Gm and Inv systems of immunoglobulin allotypes.

436. The answer is B. *(Davis, ed 2. p 429.)* The hinge region exists between C_{H1} and C_{H2}. C_{H4} and C_{H5} do not exist in IgG. Amino acid sequences are distinctive for each heavy chain class and subclass, probably contributing to the distinctive biologic properties of the various immunoglobulins.

437. The answer is E. *(Davis, ed 2. pp 459-460, 466. Gell, ed 3. pp 449-464.)* T cells do not differentiate into plasma cells. Rather, B cells are the progenitors of plasma cells, and T cells help them in this progression.

438. The answer is A. *(Davis, ed 2. p 446.)* The concentrations in mg/ml of serum for each of the listed subclasses of immunoglobulins are: IgG-1, 8 mg/ml; IgG-2, 4 mg/ml; IgG-3, 1 mg/ml; IgG-4, 0.4 mg/ml; and IgA-1, 3.5 mg/ml. Serum concentrations of other antibodies are: IgA-2, 0.4 mg/ml; IgM, 1 mg/ml; IgD, 0.03 mg/ml; and IgE, 1×10^{-4} mg/ml.

439. The answer is E. *(Davis, ed 2. pp 446, 538. Gell, ed 3. pp 766-768.)* IgE molecules sensitize human mast cells and are responsible for atopic allergy. Guinea pigs, by contrast, are sensitized by guinea pig IgE and gamma-1 globulin, and by human IgG-1, -3, and -4.

440. The answer is B. *(Davis, ed 2. pp 477-479.)* In the mouse, immune response genes governing the ability of inbred strains to respond to some antigens are located in the chromosome between genes coding for serologically defined K and D antigens of the H-2 histocompatibility complex. The genes govern the ability of a mouse to make circulating antibodies in response to booster injections of "limited" antigens. The antigens are limited in (1) being given in small doses, e.g., ovalbumin, (2) possessing few structural determinants, e.g., synthetic polypeptides, and (3) having only a few structural determinants which differ from the test antigen, e.g., natural alloantigens such as the histoincompatibility antigens.

441. The answer is C. *(Davis, ed 2. p 618.)* The haplotypes of the father are 3,7 and 25,12. The haplotypes of the mother are 1,8 and 3,9. The brother inherited the 1,8 and 25,12 haplotypes. Of the various histotypes given, only C combines haplotypes of both parents in this instance 3,9 from the mother, and 3,7 from the father.

442. The answer is C. *(Davis, ed 2. p 480. Gell, ed 3. pp 317-319.)* Disease susceptibility is thought to be more closely linked to the immune response gene than to HL-A genes themselves. The analysis of human histocompatibility gene linkage to human immune response genes has lagged far behind the analysis of the murine model, but using the mouse as a model it may be anticipated that some of the observed associations stem from the proximity of histocompatibility genes and immune response genes.

443. The answer is D. *(Davis, ed 2. p 372.)* In tube four the maximum precipitate is observed, occurring at approximate antigen-antibody equivalence. In tubes one through three antibody excess occurs, and in tube five antigen excess occurs.

444. The answer is D. *(Davis, ed 2. pp 420, 616-618.)* Linkage disequilibrium occurs when the concurrent expressions of alleles of two loci have a greater than statistically predicted association and, therefore, a presumed selective advantage.

445. The answer is A. *(Davis, ed 2. p 460.)* Granulocytes constitute about 70 percent of white cells in a peripheral blood smear. Macrophages are rarely seen. Of the lymphocytes, T cells constitute approximately 70 percent, B cells about 25 percent, and null (neither T nor B) cells about 5 percent.

446. The answer is A. *(Davis, ed 2. p 618.)* O+ platelets will not be rejected by an AB+ person on the basis of ABO grouping. HL-A identity rules out rejection on the basis of HL-A histotype.

447. The answer is B. *(Davis, ed 2. pp 618-619. Gell, ed 3. p 529.)* Surgical techniques for transplanting human hearts are well developed. The principal objection has been the relatively fast rejection time of transplanted hearts in spite of intensive immunosuppressive efforts.

448. The answer is E. *(Davis, ed 2. pp 617-618. Gell, ed 3. p 511.)* The most common allograft is transplantation of skin. Although graft rejection can be anticipated within a few weeks, the temporary benefit in control of fluid loss and infection is frequently life saving.

449. The answer is C. *(Davis, ed 2. p 459.)* Mouse T cells do not express the PC (plasma cell) surface alloantigen, but express histocompatibility (H-2) antigens, as do human T cells. The Ly and TL alloantigen systems are now intricately described, and allow for differentiation of functional subclasses of the T cell population. Theta antigen, shared by brain and T cells, is an analog of T cell antigens in other species, which may be defined by isoimmunization.

450. The answer is A. *(Davis, ed 2. pp 387-388.)* In the first bleed pattern shown, cross reaction between X and antigen A is recognizable only by the shortening of the precipitin band between 1 and X on the A well side (relative to the band going directly into the normal saline well). In the second bleed pattern, full cross reaction of X and A is apparent. No other cross reactions are seen.

451. The answer is E. *(Davis, ed 2. p 572. Gell, ed 3. p 856.)* Transfer factor is stable to DNase.

452. The answer is C. *(Davis, ed 2. pp 361-362.)* In a Scatchard plot, the slope of the line is equal to $-K$, as shown in the diagram. The slope here is $-2/2 \times 10^{-4}$ moles/l. K is therefore 1×10^4 l/mole.

453. The answer is D. *(Davis, ed 2. pp 361-362.)* The extrapolation to the abscissa value of $r = 4$ at infinitely high concentration C of hapten, gives the number of sites at maximal saturation. In this case, four sites.

454. The answer is C. *(Davis, ed 2. pp 410, 417-418.)* Secretory IgA is a tetravalent dimer. Fab' is the monovalent fragment of IgG. $F(ab')_2$ is the divalent fragment of IgG, missing the Fc tail of the molecule. IgE is divalent and IgM is penta- or decavalent, depending on the experimental conditions.

455. The answer is C (2, 4). *(Davis, ed 2. p 474.)* B cell functions are decreased on bursectomy: germinal centers atrophy; and plasma cells as well as circulating immunoglobulins decrease. T cell functions are relatively unaffected: circulating lymphocyte counts are maintained, and skin graft rejection time is unaltered.

456. The answer is A (1, 2, 3). *(Davis, ed 2. p 389.)* Cross-reaction of X with material in wells 1, 2, and 3 is shown. X does not cross-react with 4. A second component is present in wells 1 and 2 which does not cross-react with X or 4.

457. The answer is E (all). *(Davis, ed 2. pp 538-554. Gell, ed 3. pp 768-769, 821-843.)* In anaphylaxis, edema occurs as a result of injury to vascular endothelium. Heparin is liberated resulting in diminished coagulability of blood. Leukopenia occurs because leukocytes adhere to walls of capillaries, especially in the lungs, under the influence of several agents, including complement cascade fragments. Histamine causes smooth muscle spasm.

458. The answer is D (4). *(Davis, ed 2. pp 504-506. Gell, ed 3. p 661.)* Passive immunity in newborn infants results from the in utero transfer of maternal immunoglobulin G via the placenta, and to a lesser extent, from immunoglobulins present in colostrum in some species. The protection against common infections (especially bacterial) afforded by such passive immunity has a half-life of approximately three to four weeks, and reaches a nadir at approximately three months, when endogenous production of antibodies in the newborn assumes a normal rate. IgM and IgA multimers are too large to pass the placental barrier, and IgD and IgE exist in such minute quantities in the maternal circulation that their passage is of little protective consequence to the newborn.

459. The answer is E (all). *(Gell, ed 3. pp 1702-1707. Jawetz, ed 11. p 151.)* The antibody response to a given antigen depends upon all of the factors cited. In addition, it should be mentioned that prior exposure of a subject to an antigen may allow an amnestic secondary response to occur months and even years later. Adjuvants may heighten the response of a subject to an antigen when inherent antigenicity is suboptimal.

460. The answer is A (1, 2, 3). *(Gell, ed 3. pp 766-774. Jawetz, ed 11. p 165.)* Anaphylactic reactions result from triggering of histamine-containing mast cells and basophils with specific cytotropic antibodies. When cell-bound antibodies react with antigen, degranulation and release of pharmacologic mediators (kinins, histamines) occurs and leads to local or systemic reactions. Arthus reactions, however, require larger amounts of antibody which complex with antigens to fix complement and attract polymorphonuclear leukocytes. This reaction is not inhibited by antihistamines.

461. The answer is D (4). *(Gell, ed 3. pp 1084, 1168-1170, 1218-1232, 1360-1375. Jawetz, ed 11. pp 171-172, 182.)* Autoimmunity to sequestered proteins usually appears to follow injury or insult to tissues containing antigens that are normally removed from contact with the immune mechanism. Tissue antigens that are presumably normally sequestered and do not usually evoke auto-tolerance, in this circumstance provoke a humoral and cellular immune response as though they were foreign antigens. Thyroid antigens, in the case of Hashimoto's disease, evoke antithyroid antibody, as well as an infiltrate of sensitized lymphocytes. In Goodpasture's syndrome, antibodies which react with basement membrane found in lung, kidney, and elsewhere, are generated following glomerulonephritis. In thrombocytopenic purpura, normal or drug-altered platelet membranes (not sequestered antigens) elicit and become the target of the host immune response. The antigen that elicits an immune response in rheumatic fever is an antigen shared by group A beta-hemolytic streptococci and human myocardial sarcolemma.

462. The answer is D (4). *(Davis, ed 2. p 484. Gell, ed 3. pp 296-297.)* The graph shown exhibits hemagglutinating antibody responses to primary and secondary immunization with any standard antigen. In particular, it demonstrates the early, chiefly IgM response to primary immunization. Rechallenge would elicit an accelerated, chiefly IgG response which would occur on days two through five. IgM has a molecular weight of 900,000 (not 150,000) and is a pentamer (not a tetramer) that the fetus can produce quite early in gestation.

463. The answer is B (1, 3). *(Davis, ed 2. pp 372-373.)* The ascending limb of the illustrated precipitin curve "A", the antibody-excess zone, contains unreacted antibody in the supernatant solution. On the descending limb "C", or antigen-excess zone, the supernatant solution contains excess free antigen. In a monospecific system, zone "B" designates the region of maximum precipitation and the supernatant solution is free of precipitable antibody and antigen. In a complex polyspecific system, excess antigen or antibody molecules may be present at the point of maximum precipitate formation, because the optimum quantity of each antigen may be different.

464. The answer is B (1, 3). *(Davis, ed 2. p 622. Gell, ed 3. p 637.)* Carcinoembryonic antigens (CEA) comprise a variety of glycoproteins whose production is determined by genes that are expressed in normal fetal development, but not usually in adults. Malignant cells tend to lose markers of specialization and differentiation under certain circumstances; with such de-differentiation, malignant cells deriving from endoderm, especially that of the pancreas, colon, and rectum, frequently give rise to CEA. However, not all cases of colorectal carcinoma, even when very advanced, manifest CEA, and a surprising frequency of breast, and even lung tumors, may be associated with CEA.

465. The answer is B (1, 3). *(Davis, ed 2. p 459. Gell, ed 3. pp 456-465.)* B lymphocytes have cell surface immunoglobulins and an X-irradiation susceptibility much greater than that of T cells. Their peripheral blood frequency is 15 to 25 percent, while T cells make up 75 to 85 percent of peripheral blood lymphocytes. T cells, and not B cells, have theta cell surface alloantigens.

466. The answer is C (2, 4). *(Davis, ed 2. pp 408, 415, 422. Gell, ed 3. pp 285-304.)* The Inv allotypic locus is manifest on kappa chains only. Inv(1,2) is leucine-191, while Inv(3) is valine-191. Genes for kappa and lambda segregate independently. Both light chains of one IgG molecule are of the same type, except when investigators have reoxidized reduced fragments to form hybrid antibodies.

467. The answer is C (2, 4). *(Davis, ed 2. pp 411, 416. Gell, ed 3. p 288.)* IgM and IgA have J chains which appear to stabilize the immunoglobulins, but are not necessary for maintaining their polymeric structure.

468. The answer is A (1, 2, 3). *(Davis, ed 2. p 411.)* The Fab portions of immunoglobulins contain complete light chains and N-terminal fragments of heavy chains. The Fc portions contain C-terminal fragments of heavy chains and no light chains.

469. The answer is A (1, 2, 3). *(Davis, ed 2. pp 377-378, 410.)* Neither monovalent antigen, nor monovalent antibody (Fab'), can form a precipitin lattice. A closely repeating unit antigen, e.g., a polysaccharide or multi-chained polymeric protein, can bind antibody to two determinants on a single particle in a "monogamous bivalency." $F(ab')_2$ divalent antibodies can precipitate antigens as well as whole IgG molecules, though they lack Fc portions.

470. The answer is E (all) *(Davis, ed 2. pp 466, 468. Gell, ed 3. pp 458-464.)* All of the statements given apply to B lymphocytes, and all but the first apply to T cells. Plant mitogens may be used to differentiate B and T cells, as phytohemagglutinin and concanavalin A preferentially stimulate T cells.

471. The answer is B (1, 3). *(Williams, 1972. pp 1115-1117.)* Injury to the vascular endothelium is followed by adhesion of platelets to the injured site. The platelets do not adhere to the endothelial cells, but rather to connective tissue fibers, probably specifically to collagen. It has been demonstrated that the native structure of collagen is essential for its platelet-aggregating effect, and that the ϵ-amino groups of lysine in the collagen are involved in the attachment of platelets. Platelet aggregation is also induced by a basement membrane component of larger vessels. This component is apparently not collagen, since it is not digested by collagenase and has a different periodicity as determined by electron microscopy.

472. The answer is B (1, 3). *(Robbins, 1974. pp 220, 229-236.)* Serum sickness is a systemic immune disorder caused by small, soluble antigen-antibody aggregates circulating in the bloodstream. Deposition of these complexes in the renal glomerulus may lead to glomerular damage. Circulating nuclear autoantibodies and free nuclear antigens are responsible for the nephritis of systemic lupus erythematosus.

473. The answer is E (all). *(Davis, ed 2. p 355.)* All of the statements given about haptens are true. Drug allergies involving haptenic determinants require sensitization to a modified form of the drug coupled to an endogenous protein (carrier).

474. The answer is A (1, 2, 3). *(Davis, ed 2. p 463.)* T cells bearing sheep erythrocyte receptors may be removed from peripheral blood by formation of sheep cell rosettes and subsequent sedimentation. Nylon fiber columns bind IgG-bearing B lymphocytes and allow T cells to pass. A cell separator also separates pools of immunoglobulin-bearing B cells and non-immunoglobulin-bearing T cells. Anti-theta serum and complement may be used to prepare B cells by lysis of T cells, but T cells are lost by this method.

475. The answer is E (all). *(Davis, ed 2. pp 419-420.)* All of the molecules listed have allelic variants in which single amino acid substitutions occur, giving rise to antigenically distinct molecules.

476. The answer is E (all). *(Davis, ed 2. pp 484-485.)* All of the possibilities cited may occur with repeated immunization. Higher titers of all antibodies are observed, and as priming is repeated, the immune response recruits B cells of progressively greater affinity. However, as affinity rises cross-reactivity also rises, and the response becomes wider and wider in specificity. As the multiplicity of antigenic sites detected per reacting particle (Dnp-ovalbumin) increases, the avidity increases. In addition to shifts in the class of immunoglobulin synthesized in response to an antigen (M to G), shifts also may occur in the idiotype of antibody.

477-481. The answers are: 477-D, 478-B, 479-C, 480-A, 481-E. *(Jawetz, ed 11. p 147.)* IgA can exist as a monomer (7 S), a dimer (9 S), or a trimer (11 S). IgM exists as a pentamer except under conditions of reduction. IgG, IgD, and IgE are found only as monomers.

482-486. The answers are: 482-B, 483-C, 484-B, 485-D, 486-B. *(Davis, ed 2. pp 506-509. Gell, ed 3. pp 656-668.)* Immunodeficiency disorders can be divided into categories depending upon whether the defect is one which involves both B and T cells (bone-marrow derived, and thymus derived), or preponderantly one or the other. Swiss-type hypogammaglobulinemia, ataxia-telangiectasia, the Wiskott-Aldrich syndrome, and severe combined immunodeficiency all involve both B and T cell defects. Infantile X-linked agammaglobulinemia involves chiefly B cells, and thymic hypoplasia chiefly T cells.

487-490. The answers are: 487-C, 488-A, 489-B, 490-D. *(Davis, ed 2. pp 378-379, 393, 396. Gell, ed 3. pp 9-12, 33.)* The Farr technique of ammonium sulfate precipitation depends upon the differential precipitation of antibody, and antigen-antibody complexes in high (40%) salt concentrations, and upon the solubility of unbound antigens at this salt concentration. By the Farr technique, titrations can determine the antigen-binding capacity, and the intrinsic association constants of antibody and antigen. The Coombs technique is a routinely employed method which allows the detection of non-agglutinating, or incomplete, antibodies by means of an antiglobulin. It is a means of amplifying reactions which would otherwise be impossible to detect by immunofluorescence or hemagglutination. The discrepancy between the amount of antigen (toxin) neutralized by a given amount of antibody when added at one time, and the much smaller neutralizing capacity of a given solution of antibody when antigen is added stepwise, was first noted and described by Danysz using the diphtheria toxin-antitoxin system. It has been attributed to the combination of antigen and antibody in different ratios, and depends upon a degree of irreversibility in this interaction; the same phenomenon is seen with precipitation, where equivalence points may depend upon the manner in which antigen and antibody are combined. Monogamous bivalency is the term applied by Karush to the nonprecipitating combination of high-affinity antibodies and antigenic determinants on the same particle. It depends upon the appearance of repetitive antigenic determinants on the same particle with which a single antibody molecule may react.

491-493. The answers are: 491-D, 492-C, 493-B. *(Davis, ed 2. pp 406, 423-425. Gell, ed 3. pp 293-294.)* In addition to heavy chain isotypes of IgG, IgA, IgM, IgD, and IgE, two light chain isotypes exist for kappa and lambda chains. Isotypes are determined by antigens of the major immunoglobulin classes found in all individuals of one species. Allotypes are differentiated by antigenic determinants which vary between individuals within a species, and are recognized by cross-immunization of individuals in a species. Allotypes include the Gm marker of IgG and the Inv marker of light chains. Idiotypes are antigenic determinants that appear only on the Fab fragments of antibodies, and appear to be localized at the ligand-binding site so that anti-idiotype antisera may block reactions with the appropriate hapten. The carbohydrate side chains of immunoglobulins are relatively nonimmunogenic. New determinants may be exposed after papain cleavage of immunoglobulins, but these determinants are not included in classification of the native molecule.

494-498. The answers are: 494-B, 495-C, 496-A, 497-E, 498-D. *(Davis, ed 2. p 426. Wintrobe, ed 7. p 1281.)* The diagnoses associated with the electrophoretic profiles shown in the question depend on: "B" the absence of a peak adjacent to albumin, where α_1-antitrypsin should appear; "C" the presence of a monoclonal gammopathy (although other features would be required to define multiple myeloma); "D" the absence of an anodal gamma peak; and "E" diffuse elevation of the gamma peak.

Bibliography

Ames, G. *J Biol Chem* 249 (1974):634.

Baserga, R. *Life Sciences* 15 (1974):1057-1071.

Beeson, P.B., and McDermott, W., eds. *Cecil-Loeb Textbook of Medicine*. 14th ed. 2 vols. Philadelphia: Columbia Broadcasting System, W. B. Saunders Co., 1975.

Bellanti, J. A. *Immunology*. Philadelphia: Columbia Broadcasting System, W. B. Saunders Co., 1971.

Briody, B.A., ed. *Microbiology & Infectious Disease*. New York: McGraw-Hill Book Co., 1974.

Brown, H. W. *Basic Clinical Parasitology*. 4th ed. New York: Prentice-Hall, Inc., Appleton-Century-Crofts, 1975.

Burrows, W. *Textbook of Microbiology*. 20th ed. Philadelphia: Columbia Broadcasting System, W. B. Saunders Co., 1973.

Copenhaver, W. M.; Bunge, R. P.; and Bunge, M. P. *Bailey's Textbook of Histology*. 16th ed. Baltimore: Williams & Wilkins Co., 1971.

Costlow, M., and Baserga, R. *J Cell Physiol* 82 (1973):411-420.

Farber, J.; Rovera, G.; and Baserga, R. *Biochem J* 122 (1971):189.

Faust, E.C.; Russell, P.; and Jung, R. *Craig & Faust's Clinical Parasitology*. 8th ed. Philadelphia: Lea & Febiger, 1970.

Fujimoto, W. Y.; Subak-Sharpe, J. H.; and Seegmiller, J. E. *Proc Natl Acad Sci* 68 (1971): 1516-1519.

Gell, P.G.H.; Coombs, R. R. A.; and Ladumann, P. J. *Clinical Aspects of Immunology*. 3rd ed. Oxford: Blackwell Scientific Publications, 1975.

Harvey, A. M., and Johns, R. J. *The Principles & Practices of Medicine*. 18th ed. New York: Prentice-Hall, Inc., Appleton-Century-Crofts, 1972.

Horsfall, F. L., and Tamm, I. *Viral & Rickettsial Infections of Man*. 4th ed. Philadelphia: J. B. Lippincott Co., 1965.

Ishikawa, et al. *J Cell Biol* 43 (1969):312.

Jawetz, E.; Melnick, J. L.; and Adelberg, E. A. *Review of Medical Microbiology.* 11th ed. Los Altos: Lange Medical Publications, 1974.

Jones, T. H., and Kennedy, E. P. *J. Biol Chem* 244:5981-5987.

Lehninger, A. *Biochemistry.* New York: Worth Publishers, Inc., 1970.

Malawista, S. E., and Weiss, M. C. *Proc Natl Acad Sci* 71 (1974):927-931.

Merritt, H. H., ed. *A Textbook of Neurology.* 5th ed. Philadelphia: Lea & Febiger, 1973.

Nicolson, G. L., and Singer, S. J. *J Cell Biol* 60 (1974):236-248.

Paul, L. W., and Juhl, H. L. *The Essentials of Roentgen Interpretation.* 3rd ed. New York: Harper & Row Publications, Inc., Harper Medical Department, 1972.

Robbins, S. L. *Pathologic Basis of Disease.* Philadelphia: Columbia Broadcasting System, W. B. Saunders Co., 1974.

Rubin, C. S.; Dancis, J.; Yip, L. C.; Nowinski, R. C.; and Balis, M. E. *Proc Natl Acad Sci* 68 (1971):1461.

Tobey, R. A. *J Cell Physiol* 79 (1972):259-265.

Tobey, R. A., and Ley, K. D. *Cancer Res* 31 (1971):46.

Van Gool, A. P., and Nanninga, N. *J Bacteriol* 108 (1971):474-481.

Vogel, A.; Risser, R.; and Pollack, R. J. *J Cell Physiol* 82 (1973):181-188.

Williams, W. J.; Beutler, E.; Erslev, A. J.; and Rundles, R. W. *Hematology.* New York: McGraw-Hill Book Co., 1972.

Wilson, E. O.; Eisner, T.; Metzenberg, R.; Susman, M.; Boggs, W.; Briggs, W.; O'Brien, R.; and Dickerson, R. *Life on Earth.* Sunderland: Sinauer Associates, Inc., 1973.

Wintrobe, M. M.; Thorn, G. W.; Adams, R. D.; Braunwald, E.; Isselbacher, K. J.; and Petersdorf, R. G. *Harrison's Principles of Internal Medicine.* 7th rev. ed. New York: McGraw-Hill Book Co., 1974.